LANGUAGE, LOGIC AND MATHEMATICS

NEW SCIENCE SERIES

General Editor

SIR GRAHAM SUTTON, C.B.E., D.Sc., LL.D., F.R.S.

LANGUAGE
LOGIC
AND
MATHEMATICS

C. W. KILMISTER
M.Sc., Ph.D.

*Professor of Mathematics, King's College,
London*

THE ENGLISH UNIVERSITIES PRESS LIMITED

ST. PAUL'S HOUSE WARWICK LANE
LONDON · E.C.4

To the memory of Kenneth Gravett,
who taught me the importance of
much that is in this book.

First printed 1967

Copyright © 1967
C. W. Kilmister

*Printed and Bound in Great Britain for the
English Universities Press Ltd., at the Pitman Press, Bath*

EDITOR'S FOREWORD

New Science Series

THE aim of the New Science Series is to provide authoritative accounts of topics chosen from the wide range of modern science. The series includes books by experts in the physical, biological and social sciences. In the selection of titles and in the treatment the needs of the reader who has a lively curiosity about the world around him, and is prepared to make a conscious effort to understand the thoughts and achievements of specialists, have been kept to the fore. Although special attention has been given to the younger generation, it is hoped that the series will also be of interest and value to more mature minds.

These books have been written to attract a wide audience. In an age in which life is increasingly affected by scientific discovery it seems essential that the practitioners should endeavour to make clear, in part if not in whole, the aims and implications of their work. It is hoped that the New Science Series will make a contribution to this end.

O.G.S.

PREFACE

In the present century, studies which have been made in the foundations of mathematics have given us all something to think about in everyday life and in ordinary language. Unfortunately, these studies have often been couched in very technical language, and have required a very sophisticated knowledge of mathematics to appreciate them. The purpose of the present book is to explain just enough mathematics in simple terms for a real understanding of the modern developments. As well as my indebtedness to the books of H. Weyl, E. W. Beth, and S. C. Kleene, I should like to express my thanks to my colleagues at King's College, who first stimulated my interest in these matters, and to successive generations of Extra-Mural audiences, who forced me to express the ideas more clearly.

C.W.K.

CONTENTS

CONTENTS

1 INTRODUCTION

THIS BOOK is concerned with a number of problems which arise when we try to analyse what we mean by the idea of "meaning", and when we try to make the languages which we employ more precise than ordinary everyday speech. Because the most notable attempts at precision of expression occur in mathematics, which is simply a highly specialised language constructed to be as exact as possible, we shall be much concerned here with the foundations of mathematics. The word language is here used in a rather more general sense than is common. By a language we shall mean any set of rules, and a collection of entities called the vocabulary, which we use, according to the rules, in describing something which is not part of the language itself. Ordinary language is a language in this sense, although the rules (the ordinary rules of grammar) and the vocabulary are not precisely defined. We can, if we wish, make a more precise language which is rather like ordinary language, by limiting the vocabulary to some particular edition of the Concise Oxford Dictionary and stating explicitly all the rules of grammar which we shall allow ourselves to employ. However, there is little advantage in that particular kind of preciseness.

Another example of a language is ordinary arithmetic. Here the vocabulary consists of the numbers and a number of signs, like those for addition and division. Arithmetic is not able to talk about such a wide variety of things outside itself as ordinary English; it is in fact only able to discuss things for which a numerical value may be said to exist. However, the enormous development of mathematics over the last 200 years has shown us what a very wide range of things are open to arithmetical description. For reasons which will be appreciated later, arithmetic plays a central role in the discussions in the present book.

Another example of a language is the more complicated structure used by mathematicians for discussion of problems in logic. Such formal languages will be considered in a later chapter. In all of these cases the central problem is to explain the real significance of such statements as " $2+3=5$ means that, if there are two groups, of 2 and 3 apples on a table, then there are 5 apples on the table". The difficulty which we are confronted with here is that the arithmetical statement (or, more generally, the statement in the formalised language) is "cut off" from the everyday world in which apples and tables exist. In the theory which interprets the statements of a formalised language, we come upon difficulties of a kind which have not yet been surmounted, but whose discovery was certainly one of the greatest achievements of human thought in the present century.

Although we have defined languages as systems which can "talk about" something outside themselves, we have left open the question of whether a language can also talk about itself. This turns out to be a fundamental property of very great interest in a language. English, for example, is a language which can certainly talk about itself, as the many books in English on the English language, its grammar and its literature, testify. At first sight it seems as if arithmetic is not able to talk about itself. This turns out to be incorrect. The fact is that arithmetic, and any formal language which includes arithmetic has an important difference from simpler mathematical structures. This difference has the result that the more complex structures are able to talk about themselves; because of this they become involved in certain paradoxical situations. An example of such a paradox which will play a basic part in our later discussions is provided in ordinary English by the sentence

> The sentence in a box on this page is false.

The paradox to which this gives rise can be seen if we suppose this sentence to be true, for then it asserts its own validity, which contradicts itself, whereas if instead we suppose the sentence to be false, this means that the sentence in a box on this page is not false, and we again have a contradiction. The two essential features of this essentially simple "language problem" are: (i) That the language has such a structure that it can talk about its own sentences (here we have shortened such a description by the device of using a box; the reader can work out for himself how such self-description could equally well be given with the use of more words in ordinary English sentences). (ii) Ideas of *truth* and *falsehood* have to be used.

We might suppose that the idea of truth is very self-evident, and can give rise to no difficulties, so that we would put all the blame for the paradox onto the self-reference. However, the experience of philosophers in the last 2,000 years has in fact led us to view the concepts of true and false as very subtle ones which have to be used with considerable care, so that both these essential features will have to be looked at in more detail in connexion with the paradox.

Before going any further we ought to clear away some of the aspects of language which we shall not be concerned with at all in this book. The principal aspect which does not concern us is that typified by the poet. Language in poetry is used to great effect in a mysterious process which we are very far from understanding. Our reason for disregarding such things in the present book is not because of their lack of importance, but because we want to confine ourselves to phenomena which we have some hope of clarifying.

As an example of the use of language of the kind which we have no intention of discussing, we could consider the moment in "Hamlet" after Marcellus has said that on Christmas Eve ghosts do not walk, and Horatio replies:

> So I have heard and do in part believe it.
> But, look, the morn in russet mantle clad,
> Walks o'er the dew of yon high eastern hill;
> Break we our watch up.

In this wonderful passage (to which my attention was drawn by T. S. Eliot in his "Poetry and Drama"), an important part is played by the fact that in the first line a plain statement of fact is made. This is followed and contrasted with a poetical passage of great colour and beauty, and another contrast follows with what is little more than a shout of command—consisting of words of one syllable. A similar example of this aspect of language which we shall not discuss is provided by Lady Macbeth's remark "Who would have thought the old man to have had so much blood in him?". In this passage all the words are again of one syllable, and it has the appearance of a simple factual statement, but arising as it does in the play, it has an overwhelming effect on the audience.

Questions of meaning in language and discussions to clarify our use of language interested the Greeks—especially Socrates. We have of course only second-hand records of Socrates' philosophy, since he philosophised in discussions in the market-place, not by writings, and we have to rely on the writings of Plato and Xenophon, who probably give us a very partial account. However, in Plato's case we have what amounts to a full account of a kind of compound person: Socrates-as-interpreted-by-Plato, and this compound person was extremely interested in analysing the meaning of words.

It would be too lengthy to quote at length here, but the reader who has studied some of Plato's dialogues—for example, almost any part of the "Republic"—would find Socrates trying to answer such problems as "What constitutes good government?" by a careful analysis of what we mean by "good" (see, for example Book VI of the "Republic"). A shorter example of the kind of argument used is provided in the first book where Socrates undertakes the investigation of the word "justice" (and so of the *concept* "justice") with the words (Davies and Vaughan's translation):

> Come then, Thrasymachus, said I, let us start anew, and oblige us by answering: Do you assert that a perfect injustice is more profitable than an equally perfect justice?
>
> Most decidedly I do; and I have said why. Pray how do you describe them under another aspect? Probably you call one of them a virtue, and the other a vice?
>
> Undoubtedly.
>
> That is, justice a virtue and injustice a vice?
>
> A likely thing, my facetious friend, when I assert that injustice is profitable, and justice the reverse.
>
> Then what do you say?
>
> Just the contrary.
>
> Do you call justice a vice?
>
> No; but I call it very egregious good nature.
>
> Then do you call injustice ill nature?
>
> No I call it good policy.
>
> Do you think, Thrasymachus, that the unjust are positively wise and good?

One thing that we should notice here about such studies of meaning, is that the idea of meaning is clearly to be taken in a more general sense than in everyday life. It is not the meaning of certain Greek words which is in question here, since the whole of Plato's argument translates perfectly well into English. It is some generalised meaning of language which is being dealt with, of English words, Greek words, or the words of any other natural language.

Another important lesson to be drawn from the reading of the "Republic" is that ordinary language—even when not poetical—is still a very weak instrument for getting at the truth about something; especially is this so in the hands of an unscrupulous questioner. There is no doubt of the honesty and sincerity of Socrates, though the same cannot be said for all the Greek philosophers who discoursed in the market place at about the same time. But even Socrates is not above twisting his opponent's arguments round by ambiguities until the opponent subsides with some such remark as the following (from Book I of the "Republic"):

And undoubtedly a man is well able to guard an army, when he has also a talent for stealing the enemy's plans and all his other operations.

Certainly.

That is to say, a man can guard expertly whatever he can thieve expertly.

So it would seem.

Hence, if the just man is expert in guarding money, he is also expert in stealing it.

I confess the argument points that way.

Then, to all appearance, it turns out that the just man is a kind of thief: a doctrine which you have probably learnt from Homer, with whom Autolycus, the maternal grandfather of Odysseus, is a favourite, because, as the poet says, he outdid all men in thievishness and perjury. Justice therefore, according to you, Homer, and Simonides, appears to be a kind of art of stealing, whose object, however, is to help one's friends and injure one's enemies. Was not this your meaning?

Most certainly it was not, he replied; but I no longer know what I did mean.

Arguments of this sort, which are very much like the arguments used nowadays by politicians, are possible because of the imprecise nature of ordinary language. Words can be used in slightly different senses, and this slight difference may be crucial to the understanding of a passage. For this reason much of this book will be taken up with a more formal language, which has little in common with ordinary speech.

The difficulties confronting one in arguing in ordinary language have increased rather than diminished since the time of the Greeks. Before coming to modern times, it is as well to spend a little time with a philosopher who pushed ordinary language as far as it could reasonably be expected to go—Kant. Here the reader is recommended to try part of "The Critique of Pure Reason", especially the passages describing the antinomies of pure reason (here "antinomy" is simply another word for a paradox). In these passages Kant brings forward two arguments, both superficially plausible, leading to exactly opposite conclusions about a number of general facts. We may consider in detail part of the first antinomy which begins (Meiklejohn's translation of the second edition):

THESIS

The world has a beginning in time, and is also limited in regard to space.

PROOF

Granted, that the world has no beginning in time; up to every given moment of time, an eternity must have elapsed, and therewith passed away an infinite series of successive conditions or states of things in the world. Now the infinity of a series consists in the fact, that it never can be completed by means of a successive synthesis. It follows that an infinite series already elapsed is impossible, and that consequently a beginning of the world is a necessary condition of its existence. And this was the first thing to be proved.

Kant then continues with the second part of the proof, relating to space. At the same time, in a parallel column, he sets out:

Antithesis

The world has no beginning, and no limits in space, but is, in relation both to time and space, infinite.

PROOF

For let it be granted, that it has a beginning. A beginning is an existence which is preceded by a time in which the thing does not exist. On the above supposition, it follows that there must have been a time in which the world did not exist, that is, a void time. But in a void time the origination of a thing is impossible; because no part of any such time contains a distinctive condition of being, in preference to that of non-being (whether the supposed thing originate of itself, or by means of some other cause). Consequently, many series of things may have a beginning in the world, but the world itself cannot have a beginning, and is, therefore, in relation to past time, infinite.

The reader who studies these antinomies will soon become convinced that the difficulty lies in the attempt to express extraordinarily complex concepts by means of ordinary everyday language. Everyday language is a beautiful instrument for describing everyday things, but as soon as we try to use it in a more abstract way we run into difficulties of the kind exemplified by these passages of Kant.

While discussing Kant it is appropriate to mention his views on mathematics, since he is largely responsible for a view, currently widely held, of mathematics as an exact and well-defined science, existing independently of man's efforts, in which every problem has a unique solution if only we know how to find it. Mention of mathematics in this sense is to be found in the earlier parts of "The Critique of Pure Reason". For example:

> Mathematical science affords us a brilliant example, how far, independently of all experience, we may carry out *a priori* knowledge. It is true that the mathematician occupies himself with objects and cognitions only in so far as they can be represented by means of intuition. But this circumstance is easily overlooked, because the said intuition can itself be given *a priori*, and therefore is hardly to be distinguished from a mere pure conception.

In this passage Kant means by *a priori* knowledge that knowledge (if it exists) which is independent of all experience. In the next passage the distinction between *analytical* and *synthetical* judgements is that between those in which a property is stated to belong to an object because of the nature of the object (i.e. as a matter of definition) and those in which an object is stated to have a certain property, although it might quite well not have had.

> Mathematical judgements are always synthetical. Hitherto this fact, though incontestably true and very important in its consequences, seems to have escaped the analysts of the human mind, nay, to be in complete opposition to all their conjectures. For as it was found that mathematical conclusions all proceed according to the principle of contradiction (which the nature of every apodeictic certainty requires), people became persuaded that the fundamental principles of the science also were recognised and admitted in the same way. But the notion is fallacious; for although a synthetical proposition can certainly be discerned by means of the principle of contradiction, this is possible only when another synthetical proposition precedes, from which the latter is deduced, but never of itself.

A little further on, he continues:

> Arithmetical propositions are therefore always synthetical, of which we may become more clearly convinced by trying large numbers. For it will thus become quite evident, that turn and twist our conceptions

as we may, it is impossible, without having recourse to intuition, to arrive at the sum total or product by means of the mere analysis of our conceptions. Just as little is any principle of pure geometry analytical. "A straight line between two points is the shortest", is a synthetical proposition. For my conception of straight contains no notion of quantity, but is merely qualitative. The conception of the shortest is therefore wholly an addition, and by no analysis can it be extracted from our conception of a straight line. Intuition must therefore here lend its aid, by means of which and thus only, our synthesis is possible.

This view of mathematics is, in view of the discoveries described later in the present book, a quite untenable one. We now know that any mathematical system which is sufficiently complicated to include elementary arithmetic (here and later elementary arithmetic will mean the arithmetic of the positive integers and zero), will always contain statements which cannot be deduced in the system although they are evidently true. Thus there will always be a large element of undecideability about mathematical results, and Kant's view of mathematics as an ideal science to which the others might aspire in being built on synthetic *a priori* truths, is one which we can no longer accept.

Before launching on the detailed work of the book, we will give a sketch of the developments in mathematics which have been the main cause of the work in formal languages which we are discussing. The interest in the basic ideas of mathematics (for example, in the questions of what mathematics is, what it means for a mathematical entity to exist, and so on) was not an example of wilful cynicism and questioning on the part of mathematicians in a subject where all was going well. From time to time acute difficulties and paradoxes have arisen in mathematics. The most recent occasion was at the end of the 19th century, when serious paradoxes arose in the theory of infinite sets put forward by Cantor (these are described in Chapter 4 of the present book). The first serious attempt to avoid such paradoxes was that of A. N. Whitehead and B. Russell in Cambridge around 1910 and onwards. Their aim was to find a secure foundation for mathematics, and having laid this foundation they felt confident that the paradoxes would disappear. We can, without being fanciful, see something of the optimism of Edwardian England in this outlook. However their very grand scheme, although it issued in a magnificent 3-volume work, "Principia Mathematica", ended in a disaster which was as serious for their particular aims as the disastrous end of the Edwardian era in the life of the country and Europe as a whole. The Whitehead-Russell view and its failure will be discussed in Chapters 5, 6, and 7.

Independently of Whitehead and Russell, Hilbert in Zürich had the idea of clarifying the foundations of mathematics in a much less ambitious way. Whereas Whitehead and Russell aimed at establishing the truth of the whole system by means of some previously laid sure foundations, Hilbert hoped to avoid the paradoxes by following the well-known scientific procedure of splitting the problem into two parts, and tackling them separately. He hoped to be able to ignore, at least to start with, all questions involving truth and falshood, since he knew that these had given much trouble to philosophers in the past. He aimed only at establishing the *consistency* and *completeness* of sets of axioms as explained in Chapter 8. Here consistency implies that one cannot prove both a result and the contradictory result. Completeness means that sufficient axioms have been given, so that all the results which "ought" (in some sense) to be deducible actually can be deduced. Hilbert and his school in Zürich made surprisingly great advances in this direction until 1930. In 1930, as is explained in Chapter 9, Gödel showed that the Hilbert ideal was untenable. We are now in a situation in which we do not quite know how to put matters right.

In the last chapter we shall try to enter into more detail about one particular technique for investigation of what can possibly be constructed in a formal system (in particular, arithmetic), because it is only by going into specific techniques that we can get the real flavour of such investigations (as distinct from their importance).

2 GREEK LOGIC

IN THIS chapter we shall discuss at some length the earliest attempt
to construct an artificial language for the purpose of avoiding con-
tradictions in arguments, paradoxes, and fallacies. This attempt by
the Greeks was put into a complete form by Aristotle. In the succeed-
ing 1,000 years or so various minor additions were made to his
system. It is of no interest for our present purpose to distinguish
between the contributions of Aristotle and those of his successors,
and we shall frequently use his name to describe the whole system,
even though this may include things which he would have rejected.

The basis of Aristotle's logic is the assumption that all correct
argument can be analysed into sentences of one particular form.
This form is known as the subject-predicate proposition. (By a
proposition is simply meant a sentence which is either true or false.)
Aristotle assumes that all such sentences occurring in an argument
are of the form of two entities, one called the subject, the other
the predicate, connected by a connective—usually in English the
word "is" or "is not". For example, "All men are mortal", "Some
Italian communists are Catholics", "No mammals are hatched
from eggs", "Some mammals do not live on land" (for example,
whales).

There are two great objections to beginning logic in this way.
In the first place Aristotle's assumption is clearly false. We have
many examples of arguments which are perfectly correct and which
cannot be analysed in this way; or if they can, only very artificially.
For example, almost no mathematical arguments can be analysed
in this way. Secondly, even if it were true that arguments could be
broken down into subject-predicate propositions, this breaking down
is the difficult part of assessing the correctness or otherwise of the
arguments. Once it has been done, the remaining difficulties of
deciding on the validity of the arguments are very minor ones. Thus
Aristotle's theory—although it certainly deserves our respect as a
first attempt—begs the most important question. Anyone who doubts
this should try to analyse one of the passages from Kant which was

discussed in the last chapter. For the moment we shall ignore the difficulties of Aristotle's system, and describe its actual mechanism.

The subject and predicate of a proposition will be denoted by S and P. The next step is to classify the kind of propositions which arise. Aristotle distinguishes four kinds of proposition. In the first place the proposition may be affirmative or negative, depending on whether the connective is "is" or "is not". Next he considers the possibility of what is known as *quantification* of the subject; that is to say, the subject may be considered to be all members of a certain class, or only some members. This gives the four propositions:

SaP: all S is P

SeP: no S is P

SiP: some S is P

SoP: some S is not P.

Aristotle deliberately refrains from quantifying the predicate. If he were to allow "all" or "some" to occur before P as well as before S, he could produce superficially different forms of proposition. A great argument raged for a time amongst the Greek logicians about whether something was being disregarded here or not. As we shall see later, Aristotle was correct in the sense that the new propositions produced by quantifying the predicate are all equivalent to one of the above four.

We may notice, however, that in some of these propositions (viz. the middle two) the predicate is quantified in effect, since the two statements SeP and PeS are completely equivalent, as are SiP and PiS.

We have now dealt in a summary fashion with Aristotle's doctrine of propositions. An *argument* for Aristotle (or, indeed, for any later logician) is a collection of propositions related in a certain way. However, he then further assumes that correct argument can, possibly with some difficulty, be analysed into a succession of basic arguments each involving only three propositions. For example, "All men are mortal, Socrates is a man, therefore Socrates is mortal". Two of these propositions are the premises of the argument, the third is the conclusion. We shall use S and P for the subject and predicate of the conclusion. In order that an inference can take place there must be some other entity involved in the two premises. This other entity is called the middle term, and denoted by M.

In the example above, Socrates is the subject, the class of mortal beings is the predicate, and the middle term is the class of all men. One of the premises involves M and P, and this is called the major premiss and is always written first. The other one involves S and M, is called the minor premiss and is written second. This collection of 3 propositions is known as a syllogism. (As a matter of fact Aristotle and his successors did occasionally consider forms of argument more complicated than a syllogism which could not be analysed into a syllogism, but for the most part they confined themselves to the syllogism.) In many ways this analysis of argument is very appealing, especially to the scientist. The first statement in our example can be regarded as a general assertion of the same kind as the assertion in a scientific theory. The second statement then supplies the data of the particular problem considered. The conclusion then results from applying the general propositions of the theory to this particular problem.*

The great achievement of Aristotle was to find all the valid kinds of syllogism. The fact that there are a considerable number arises as follows. Firstly, S and P occur in their respective premises either as subject or predicate, the middle term being the corresponding other part of the premise. This gives us 4 combinations of positions of S and P, known as the 4 figures of the syllogism, in the following way:

I	II	III	IV
MP	PM	MP	PM
SM	SM	MS	MS
SP	SP	SP	SP

In each figure the gap between the subject and predicate of each proposition has to be filled by one of the vowels a, e, i, and o. There are then 256 possible syllogisms which can be written down, but most of these are invalid in the sense that the conclusion does not follow from the premises and we have to find out how to select the valid forms (or *moods*).

Let us consider how to do this in one particular case which was regarded by Aristotle himself as a kind of ideal standard to which one could aim to reduce other syllogisms, and which is in any case

* I am indebted to Sir Graham Sutton for this remark.

the simplest to consider. This is the syllogism in which the connective is *a* in every case, and the syllogism is in the first figure. It therefore has the form

$$MaP$$
$$SaM$$
$$\overline{SaP}.$$

We can represent this syllogism, and any other one, by a convenient figure of three circles in a general position relative to each other. The circles represent in a familiar way the set of things defined by one of the quantities *S, M,* or *P.* In *Figure 1* the various regions into which the plane is divided by the circles have been numbered. Let us consider what the premises of this syllogism imply about these regions. The major premiss clearly says that regions 3 and 5 are empty. Similarly the minor premiss says that regions 1 and 7 are empty. From knowing that regions 1, 3, 5, and 7 are all empty, we have to construct a statement not involving the middle term *M.* A glance at the figure shows that such a statement is that 3 and 7

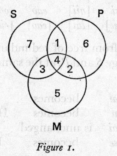

Figure 1.

are empty, which is equivalent to the conclusion "All *S* is *P*". This mood of the syllogism is therefore easily justified by the circle diagrams. The reader who cares can try justifying the other moods, given in the following list as derived by other means by Aristotle and his successors:

First figure   *aaa, eae, aii, eio*
Second figure   *eae, aee, eio, aoo*
Third figure   *aai, iai, aii, eao, oao, eio*
Fourth figure   *aai, aee, iai, eao, eio.*

This list is summarised by the famous mnemonic, containing all the known results of the syllogism, said to occur first in the writings of Petrus Hispanus, Pope John XXI (died 1277) (though he does not claim to be the author):

Barbara, Celarent, Darii, Ferioque, *prioris*:
Cesare, Camestres, Festino, Baroko, *secundae*:
Tertia, Darapti, Disamis, Datisi, Felapton, Bokardo, Ferison, *habet*:
Quarta insuper addit Bramantip, Camenes, Dimaris, Fesapo, Fresison.

Not only are the vowels significant; the consonants *m, s, p,* and *c* explain, in a certain code, how the syllogisms in the later figures can be reduced to the first.

However the difference between some of these moods is more apparent than real. From what we said about equivalent propositions above, wherever *e* or *i* occurs in the premises we may convert one mood to another in a different figure. If we bracket redundant moods according to this, we get:

I	*aaa*	*eae*	*aii*	*eio*		
II	[*eae*]	*aee*	[*eio*]	*aoo*		
III	*aai*	*iai*	[*aii*]	*eao*	*oao*	[*eio*]
IV	*aai*	[*aee*]	[*iai*]	[*eao*]	[*eio*]	

But even this list is far from free of redundancy. If the conclusion is *e* or *i* we may interchange *S* and *P*, at the same time changing the two premises. In this way:

IV	*aai*	becomes	I	*aii*
III	*iai*	becomes	III	*aii*
III	*aai*	is unchanged		
II	*aee*	becomes	II	*eae*

leaving only

I	*aaa*	*eae*	*aii*	*eio*
II	*aoo*			
III	*aai*	*eao*	*oao*	

and no argument at all in the fourth figure.

The reader may well wonder at this point whether the wool is not being pulled over his eyes, so that he will be unable to recognise the essential triviality of all this. This opinion, which was certainly held by laymen from the Middle Ages onwards, about the teaching in the Schools is substantially correct, and the popular opinion is

well illustrated by the story (in "A hundred merry tales", an anony-
mous 16th century work known to Shakespeare) of the wealthy
franklin who sent his son to Oxford and, having him home for the
vacation, asked him what he had learnt. "I can prove that two is
three, father", replied the son. "There are two fowls in the dish in
the hearth", said the father. "Can you prove that they are three?"
"Indeed I can", returned the boy and picking up one he said "Here
is one fowl". Then picking the two up, "Here are two fowls;
and one and two makes three, *ergo* here are three fowls". "Very
good", said his father; "Now give one of those fowls to your mother,
and one to me, and you shall have the third for your supper".
The whole matter *is* very trivial, and the reader may wonder why
we devote so much space to it, and also why it has survived for so
long. To answer the second question first, we find in the statutes of
the University of Oxford in the 14th century the rule "Bachelors
and Masters of Arts who do not follow Aristotle's philosophy are
subject to a fine of 5s. for each point of divergence, as well as for
infractions of the rules of the Organon". More generally, academic
authority has had a great deal to do with the survival of this archaic
structure. Turning to the first question, it is well worth our study
because it leads on to less trivial developments in the present century
and because, although we can see now that it is trivial, it was a great
achievement in its own time.

We should make it clear exactly what is meant by the word
"trivial" here and later. When we have a problem of a mathematical
nature, or some similar kind of problem which can be put in terms
resembling mathematical ones, it may happen that we have a rule
which enables us always to find a solution to the problem. For
example, the arithmetical problem of finding the square root of a
number is a problem of this sort, because there is a (rather complicated) rule which involves dividing off the numbers in 2's from
the decimal point, using trial divisors, etc., which will always enable
us to calculate the square root to as many places as we wish. Such
problems will be called trivial to distinguish them from problems
for which we have no such universal rule, and whose solution demands
art and ingenuity. Of course we do not mean to imply that trivial
problems can necessarily be solved without a great deal of work.
The extraction of the square root of a very large number may be a
very unpleasant business indeed, but because the rule exists we know
that, given long enough, we can always do it. This meaning of the
word trivial is not completely equivalent to its use in other parts of

mathematics. Hardy, for example, calls a result trivial if it is not capable of considerable extension so that for him the criterion is not what went into the result but what it leads to. We are more concerned with having actually reached some conclusion, and so we are concerned with whether results can be reached by a uniform predetermined process or whether we can have no idea when we start what methods we should use.

The important distinction, then, is not between easy and hard problems, but between those which we know are certainly soluble whether we try to solve them or not, and those which we can only know to be soluble when we have actually solved them.

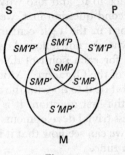

Figure 2.

Instead of drawing circles over and over again when we wish to check syllogistic arguments, it will be convenient to employ some other notation which describes the operations involved in the geometrical argument. There are two advantages in this. In the first place it saves time and paper and reduces the chances of error; more important it removes that part of the geometrical argument which is actually quite unnecessary for our purpose; that is, the sizes and accurate positions of the circles. If we have to draw a circle we must draw it a certain size and with a certain centre. But all that matters for our diagrams is that the 3 circles should all interlace like those of *Figure 1*.

In order to carry out the argument without drawing the circles, we start by labelling the regions of the plane according to the following scheme. The region inside a circle corresponding to S will be denoted by S, and that outside the circle by S'. The region common to two circles A and B will be denoted by AB. The whole set of regions can now be labelled as in *Figure 2*. The first thing which we have to do is to find out what statements about the regions are made by the four standard forms of Aristotle's propositions. Here there is no middle term to be considered, so that the four regions concerned are:

$$SP \qquad S'P \qquad SP' \qquad S'P'$$

The proposition "All S is P" means that the third of these regions is empty, and so we can denote this by

$$\overline{SP'},$$

where the bar over the symbols denotes the emptiness. Similarly the proposition "No S is P" means that the third of these regions is empty, and so can be denoted by

$$\overline{SP}.$$

The particular propositions "Some S is P" and "Some S is not P" state that the region actually has occupants, and so we can denote this by listing the region without a bar over it, and in this notation these propositions become SP and SP'.

Let us now see how to deduce the basic syllogism which we found earlier. We now have to introduce and then eliminate the middle term, so that the first premiss can be written as

$$\overline{MP'},$$

but this has to be the case whether or not S is considered. It therefore breaks up into two statements

$$\overline{SMP'} \quad \text{and} \quad \overline{S'MP'}.$$

Similarly the second premiss

$$\overline{SM'}$$

breaks up into

$$\overline{SM'P} \quad \text{and} \quad \overline{SM'P'}.$$

We now have to look at these four statements and see how we can get rid of the middle term. The middle term can be got rid of if it occurs both with and without a dash, attached in each case to the same combination of S and P. This is indeed the situation in the first and last terms and so, from these two, we can deduce

$$\overline{SP'}$$

which is the conclusion which we found before. By the help of this formalism the reader is invited to construct a proof of the various valid moods of the syllogism.

Exercises

1. Verify the following set of rules of a different kind, found by Aristotle to characterise the valid syllogisms.

   (i) The middle term must be distributed once at least (that is, must occur universally, not merely as "some M").

   (ii) A term distributed in the conclusion must be distributed in the premises.

   (iii) Both premises cannot be negative.

   (iv) A negative conclusion can only follow from a negative premise.

   (v) One premiss must be universal (that is, either a or e).

First, show that these rules must be true for valid syllogisms; in order to show conversely that every syllogism satisfying all these rules is a valid one, deduce all the syllogisms allowed by these rules, and observe that only valid ones appear.

2. (*a*) Work out how many moods of syllogism are valid if the predicate can be quantified by "all" or "some" as well as the subject. (Aristotle considered, and rejected, quantification of the predicate: "If the predicate is general, it is not correct to predicate it generally . . . as for instance in 'all men are all animals'." But this statement is probably meant merely to antagonise his opponents, the school of Megara.)

   (*b*) If the predicate is left unquantified, but the subject is quantified with "all", "most" or "some", giving two new forms

$$S\,u\,P = \text{Most } S \text{ is } P$$

$$S\,y\,P = \text{Most } S \text{ is not } P,$$

find how new valid syllogisms are produced.

3. At a certain examination all candidates who entered for Latin also entered for exactly one of French, Russian or German. All who did not enter for German entered for at least two subjects. No candidate who entered for Russian and French entered for German. All candidates who entered for neither Russian nor French, entered for Latin.

Prove that all candidates entered for exactly two languages.

3 BOOLE'S LOGIC

LOGIC DEVELOPED hardly at all after it left the hands of Aristotle until the 19th century. George Boole, born in 1815 of Irish parents in East Anglia, was the person who made the grand discovery that, by using a form of algebra different from ordinary algebra, it was possible to deduce the whole theory of the syllogism with great ease. Indeed he was able to discover errors in Aristotle's scheme, which had lain hidden for almost 2,000 years. It should be mentioned here that the algebra devised by Boole, which we shall describe here, is not the same as that going under the name of "Boolean algebra", which has become widely used in this century. Boolean algebra is a system devised by the American, Schröder, starting from Boole's system and altering it to suit particular purposes. Boole's original system is the one more suitable for discussing the syllogism.

Boole noticed that Aristotle's logic was really dealing with classes of objects; when Aristotle says "All men are mortal", it means that the class of all men is a sub-class of the class of all mortals. (Here "sub-class" means a part of the class, which may, as a special case, sometimes be the whole class.)

Boole further observed that the classes of objects which occur in Aristotle's logic can be denoted by symbols like x, y, z, subject to the ordinary rules of algebra, with the following interpretations:

(a) xy denotes the set of members of x which are also members of y.

(b) If x and y have no members in common, $x+y$ denotes the set of objects which belong either to x or to y.

(c) If x and y have common members, the symbol $x+y$ is still allowed to occur in the working, but since it is what is known by Boole as an "uninterpreted form", it must not occur in the final answer.

(d) $1-x$ denotes all the objects not belonging to the class x.

(e) $x=0$ means that the class x has no members.

It is of interest to try to relate this very interesting discovery of Boole's with the general thought at the time—not that it shows any direct influence, but because no-one ever works in a vacuum and ideas which proved fruitful in one field can often be applied in another. Boole, who was to become in 1849 the professor of mathematics in Cork, published his "Mathematical Analysis of Logic" in 1847. It shows absolutely no influence from any of the other writers on logic at the time; but it has this much in common with one other great development in mathematics—it took the symbols of algebra, which up till then had always been thought of as shorthand and generalised expressions for numbers, and it freed them from this interpretation. In 1843 Sir William Rowan Hamilton, the Astronomer-Royal of Ireland, had solved in Dublin the analogous problem of operating with directed quanties in space by inventing *quaternions*.

Let us look a little more closely at Hamilton's achievement. A directed quantity (e.g. a force or a velocity) can be written in the form

$$a = a_1 e_1 + a_2 e_2 + a_3 e_3,$$

where a is simply a shorthand form for the quantity, (a_1, a_2, a_3) are its resolved parts along 3 coordinate axes, and e_1, e_2, e_3 are three quantities of a new form. The addition of these quantities is simple; one simply adds components. The problem is to multiply two of them, a and b. By an ingenious argument Hamilton convinced himself that the product could only depend on

(a) a number $\quad Sab = -(a_1 b_1 + a_2 b_2 + a_3 b_3)$,
(b) another directed quantity

$$Vab = e_1(a_2 b_3 - a_3 b_2) + e_2(a_3 b_1 - a_1 b_3) + e_3(a_1 b_2 - a_2 b_1).$$

What else was needed for a genuine product? Hamilton could not in 1843, have formulated the question in quite that way; it was still a time when the mathematician was seen as discovering some truth about the external world, not as making more or less arbitrary assumptions. But his approach was essentially equivalent; we would answer that as many of the usual laws of algebra should hold and in particular, we would not willingly give up

$$a(bc) = (ab)c$$

$$a(b+c) = ab + ac.$$

The second of these requirements means that

$$ab = kSab + lVab$$

where k, l are numbers independent of a and b. If now the first is to be true, it must be true for any choices of e_1, e_2, e_3 for a, b, c. But since

$$e_1{}^2=e_2{}^2=e_3{}^2=-k,$$
$$e_2 e_3=-e_3 e_2=l e_1,$$

we have

$$(e_2 e_3)(e_3 e_1)=-k e_2 e_1=+k l e_3=l^2 e_1 e_2=l^3 e_3,$$

so that, supposing $l\neq 0$, $k=l^2$. We can choose l to have any value, and $l=1$ is a convenient choice, so that

$$ab=Sab+Vab.$$

Of course, Boole's problem was a completely different one from Hamilton's; both men saw that what was needed was a much more general interpretation of algebra—no longer were the symbols (and the assumptions) to be limited to what could be interpreted as ordinary numbers. (We do not want to imply that they were the only ones able to make this jump, though their results have proved most influential; in particular in any complete account the *Ausdehnungslehre* of Grassmann (1844) would have to be mentioned.)

With Boole's interpretation the reader can at once verify that the following rules must hold. (If he wishes, he could regard these as deductions from the interpretation, but if he wishes to be more formal he can regard them as axioms which are *suggested* by the interpretation which we want to make):

$$x+y=y+x \quad xy=yx$$
$$x+(y+z)=(x+y)+z \quad (xy)z=x(yz)$$
$$x(y+z)=xy+xz.$$

In addition to these rules, which have exactly the same form as those of ordinary algebra, we have the rule, obvious from the interpretation,

$$x^2=xx=x.$$

We do *not*, however, have the rule

$$2x=x+x=x,$$

which occurs in Schröder's modification of the system, since in this rule the left-hand side would be uninterpreted, and the right-hand side might be interpreted.

We can now easily write down the equations in Boole's algebra corresponding to the four forms of proposition used by Aristotle, by referring to the figure in the last chapter. We can see that:

$$SaP \text{ is } s(1-p)=0,$$
$$SeP \text{ is } sp=0,$$
$$SiP \text{ is } sp \neq 0,$$
$$SoP \text{ is } s(1-p) \neq 0,$$

where we use the small letters s and p as the corresponding symbols in Boole's algebra for the classes in Aristotle's logic. We can, however, do much better than this, for we can prove that these are essentially the only kinds of proposition which Aristotle could have considered, subject of course to his preconceived ideas about the general nature of a proposition.

We can see this as follows: a proposition consists of some relationship between s and p. In any such relationship there will be a number of terms involving various products of s and p added together and equated to zero. However, we can rearrange the order of factors in the product so that all the s's occur first and all the p's second in each term, and then we can cancel all the s's and all the p's except one of each term, by using the special property of the Boolean symbols. When we have done this, the relation must have the form

$$asp+bs+cp+d=0,$$

where a, b, c and d are four numbers which could be 1, -1, or 0 independently of each other. No other values can occur, or we should have an uninterpreted form. Now we can limit the possible occurrences of 1, -1, 0 still further by realising that any proposition of this sort, which can be interpreted, can equally be interpreted if either p or s is turned into its negative, $1-p$, or $1-s$. The effect of a change of this sort must be to give us another interpreted form. There are two cases to be considered according as a is zero or not. If a is non-zero we can take it to be 1, since if it were -1 we could multiply the whole equation through by -1.

Case 1: $a=0$.

In this case, since both s and p are to be involved, neither b nor c can be zero, and we can choose b to be 1. The possible propositions can then be completely described by the pair of numbers (c, d). When we change p to $1-p$, (c, d) becomes

$$(-c, c+d),$$

and when we change s to $1-s$, it becomes

$$(-c, \ -(1+d)).$$

We can make both these changes together, and this gives

$$(c, \ -(1+c+d)).$$

Since all of these must be interpreted, it is clear that d cannot be 1, and that $c+d$ must be -1 or 0. We are left with the following possibilities:

c	-1	1
d	0	-1

(remembering that $c=0$ is impossible, if p is to be involved). These two possibilities correspond to the two statements

$$s=p, \ s=1-p.$$

These two statements are not, it is true, of the form of any of Aristotle's propositions, but although they are different it is obvious that they simply represent very special cases, which he would not have been concerned to mention. The first one simply states the complete equivalence of s and p, so that it corresponds to the situation in which a class of objects has been given two different names although the concept is exactly the same. In the second case we have the opposite state of affairs in which one of the classes has been defined as consisting of all those things which have not the other property. It is clear from what we have said, then, that the interesting propositions will all be those in which $a=1$.

Case 2: Let us now consider the case when $a=1$.

In this case any proposition will be specified by the set of three numbers

$$(b, c, d).$$

In order that this shall be interpretable, b, c, and d must be 1, -1, or 0 independently of each other. If we carry out the same arguments as in the previous case, we find, by changing p to $1-p$, the corresponding proposition

$$[-(b+1), c, \ -(c+d)].$$

By changing s to $1-s$, we get

$$[b, -(c+1), -(b+d)],$$

and by both of these changes we get

$$[-(b+1), -(c+1), b+c+d+1].$$

All four of these propositions must be interpretable so that b and c must both be 0 or -1 independently, and when they have been chosen, d will be further restricted. Listing out the possibilities gives us the total scheme:

b	0	0	0	0	-1	-1	-1	-1
c	0	0	-1	-1	0	0	-1	-1
d	0	-1	0	1	0	1	0	1.

There appear to be eight possibilities here, of which the first one is the

$$sp = 0,$$

corresponding to the proposition "No S is P". Because of our method of argument, it is obvious that somewhere in the list there must also be the propositions

$$s(1-p) = 0, \ p(1-s) = 0, \ (1-p)(1-s) = 0,$$

which are related to the first one by various negations of the terms involved. Thus the eight possibilities which we have found fall into two sets of four, all the members of one set being essentially equivalent as far as the *form* of the proposition is concerned. One class consists of the first, third, fourth, and eighth cases, and corresponds to the propositions which we have already described. If, then, Aristotle has missed any possibilities, they must lie in the second class. A typical member of the second class is the second in the list. This has the form

$$sp = 1 \text{ implying } s = 1, \ p = 1.$$

Such a statement is a relation between s and p only in appearance. It states in fact that both s and p are properties which all the objects under consideration have. Since the second class of proposition must all be of this very simple kind, each class consists either of all objects or of none, and we are left with the only possibilities for propositions of this kind

$$SeP, \ SaP, \ \bar{S}eP, \ \bar{S}aP.$$

These four possibilities consist of two of Aristotle's propositions and two others referring to the negative of one of the classes.

It remains to consider the particular propositions of Aristotle as distinct from the universal ones. From each interpretation above, we can see that these will be given by inequalities instead of by equations. Which inequalities are possible will be determined by exactly the same argument as we have employed here to determine which equations are interpretable. Accordingly we derive the remaining two of Aristotle's forms of proposition.

We can now go on to consider Boole's treatment of the syllogism, and we shall see that his symbolic method produces a great simplification compared with Aristotle's treatment. In the first place we find that there are now really only two kinds of inferences. The various different modes found by Aristotle are simply different *interpretations* of these two basic inferences. Indeed even these two inferences are not completely different, for one of them is derived from the other. The assumption for the first inference can be written in the form

$$xy=0, \ z(1-y)=0.$$

Here x corresponds to the subject and z to the predicate of the conclusion, while y corresponds to the middle term. However, we use different letters for them because we want to consider various cases arising according as x is either s or $1-s$, and similarly with the other two letters. The second of these premises can be rewritten in the form

$$z=yz,$$

and from this it is easy to get rid of the middle term by noticing that

$$xz=x(yz)=(xy)z=0.$$

The conclusion is therefore

$$xz=0.$$

It will be sufficient for our purpose to work out the conclusions from this inference in one or two cases. Suppose, for example, that x is s, z is p, and y is m. Then the major premiss is "All p is m", and the minor premiss "No s is m". The conclusion is that "No s is p". We can write this in the Aristotelian syllogism as

$$PaM$$
$$\underline{SeM}$$
$$SeP,$$

giving one of the valid cases in the second figure. However, we could also have written the minor premiss in the form

$$MeS,$$

since x and y (that is, S and M) are involved symmetrically in it, and when we do this we derive one of the valid forms in the fourth figure. The reader should try to find which substitutions of s, $1-s$, etc., give possible syllogisms, and should verify that all the universal conclusions of Aristotle are produced from this inference.

We now have to derive the other form of inference which gives, in Aristotle's logic, particular conclusions. From our interpretation of Boolean equations we have to finish with inequalities instead of equations. We can therefore proceed by reversing the first inference and deducing from

$$xz = 0$$
$$z(1-y) \neq 0,$$
that $\qquad xy \neq 0.$

The reader will see at once that, if this conclusion did not follow, we should have a contradiction with the previous inference. In the new form of inference, however, z is to be associated with the middle term, and x and y with the subject and predicate of the conclusion. The reader may now try his hand at substituting s, $1-s$, etc., for the various letters, and so discover the particular valid forms of Aristotle. In fairness to Boole's successors we should remark that he did not himself present the particular inferences in this satisfactory way. Where we write $xy \neq 0$ he would have written $vx = vy$ (with the understanding of course, that $v \neq 0$).

We are now able to see how extremely valuable the symbolic method proves in practice. It is obvious that the working in Boole's case is very much more simple than in Aristotle's, but not only is this a saving of time but also serves to eliminate mistakes. That there was such a mistake by the successors of Aristotle which remained undetected for nearly 1,000 years is now well known. We are easily able to detect it by Boole's method. We find in fact that forms which we had listed as valid from our earlier argument, such as in the third figure, *aai* and *eao*, cannot in fact be valid inferences. The reason for this in Boole's notation is that, from the two premises

$$xy = 0$$
$$zy = 0$$

nothing can follow, since one possible way of satisfying these two premises is

$$y = 0.$$

Consider, however, what is apparently a weaker form of the first of these inferences; that is, *iai* in the third figure. How is it that this weaker inference should be still valid whilst the stronger one is shown to be a mistake? We can see how this is by writing down the weaker inference in Boole's notation. It has the form

$$
\begin{array}{ll}
M\,i\,P & mp \neq 0 \\
\underline{M\,a\,S} & \underline{m(1-s)=0} \\
S\,i\,P & sp \neq 0.
\end{array}
$$

It is now clear that the particular proposition "Some *m* is *p*", although in some respects weaker than "All *m* is *p*", is at the same time stronger in that it states the existence of objects with the property *m*. The proposition "All *m* is *p*" must be interpreted—if our logical system is to be consistent—as meaning that, if there are any objects with the property *m*, then they will also have the property *p*, whereas "Some *m* is *p*" must be taken to mean that there *are* objects which have both the properties *m* and *p*. The success of Boole's algebra in finding a fallacy which had eluded the logicians for so long, notwithstanding the trivial nature of the system, is very striking.

Examples

1. Try Example 3 of Chapter 2 by Boole's algebra, and prove that the last piece of information can be replaced by "No candidate entered for German alone".

2. Investigate the difficulties in extending Boole's algebra to the case when the subject can be quantified by "all", "most", or "some". [Hint: Try representing "Most *S* is *P*" by $sp=ks(k>\frac{1}{2})$.]

3. Carry out the procedure mentioned in the text, of substituting s, $1-s$, p, $1-p$, m, $1-m$ for the x, y, z to derive the valid syllogisms.

4 CANTOR'S SET THEORY

THE INVESTIGATIONS of Aristotle and Boole would, perhaps, have been carried no further for a long time, were it not for developments in an allied field, mathematics. As we have said, mathematics is simply an example of a rather specialised language which has been specially devised to be as clear and exact as possible. This being so, the occurrence of paradox and contradiction in it is a very chastening experience for the mathematician.

We shall begin this chapter by describing some of the difficulties which have given rise to investigations into the foundations of mathematics. The particular difficulties which form the present crisis in the subject arose at the end of the 19th century, but this was not the first occasion on which mathematics found itself in a serious situation. In the 5th century B.C., quite shortly after one of the most brilliant achievements in its history, that is, the foundation of geometry on an apparently sure deductive basis, two discoveries were made which were extremely paradoxical. Firstly it was found that not all geometrical quantities of the same kind could be expressed as a ratio of integers. For example, the diagonal of a unit square was found not to be expressible as the ratio of two integers.

If we are to prove this fact we shall need to discuss numbers in more detail and in particular to consider some of the properties of prime numbers. This will also be useful later on when we need to use these properties in order to describe systems, in terms of arithmetic, which appear to be of a more complicated kind. A prime number is a number which is not exactly divisible by any other numbers except 1. For most purposes it is convenient not to include the number 1 amongst primes, and to begin the series of primes 2, 3, 5, 7, 11 . . . . . Any number can be written as a product of prime numbers, for evidently either it is not divisible by any number exactly, in which case it is prime and the theorem is proved, or else it is so divisible and is therefore a product of two smaller numbers. We can now apply the same argument to each of these numbers separately, and continuing in this way we must eventually reach numbers which can be divided no further, that is the primes. In order to find which numbers are primes there is a device known as the sieve of Eratosthenes, in which we write down all the numbers and then strike out all multiples of 2, then all the remaining multiples of 3, then the multiples of 5 and so on. The numbers remaining are evidently primes. Although this method is one which obviously gives all the primes it is very laborious to determine whether large numbers are prime in this way, and we usually have to have recourse to other methods.

The distribution of primes is rather irregular, but if we average the distribution over large blocks of numbers a certain evenness appears and the average density of them falls slowly but significantly. Thus the first thousand numbers contain about 17 per cent of primes, the 5th thousand contain 12 per cent and the proportion has fallen to 5 per cent for the ten-thousandth thousand.

It will be important in what follows to prove that the decomposition of a number into prime factors is essentially unique. That is to say, if we arrange the factors in some definite order, say in ascending order of magnitude, there is then only one decomposition. In order to establish this result, which is known as the fundamental theorem of arithmetic, we need first to prove a subsidiary result, often called Euclid's first theorem. This theorem states that, if a prime number divides a product of two numbers, then it must divide one of the factors. At first this sounds obvious, but if we think carefully we realise that its "obviousness" is caused only by our long experience in handling numbers. It is not at all obvious that it follows from the definition of division and of prime numbers which we have given. It is then necessary to prove the theorem, and indeed it is not particularly easy to do so. We start the proof by first considering some particular sets of integers. These sets, called modules, are defined by the property that the difference of any two members of the set is itself in the set (here, by integer, we mean positive or negative integer or zero). It is clear from this definition that 0 belongs to every module, since it is the difference of any element and itself, and the negative of every element of a module also belongs to it since the negative of an element is the difference of 0 and the element. Since the negative of an element belongs, so does the difference between another element and that negative, and this is the sum of the two elements. Since the sum of any two elements belongs to the module so does twice an element (the sum of the element and itself), and similarly any multiple of an element. Finally, if x and y are any two elements, then all elements of the form $px+qy$, where p and q are positive or negative integers also belong to the module. The reader may verify the converse of this statement, i.e. that the set of all elements of the form $px+qy$ is a module. As a matter of fact these modules are something very simple, viz. all the multiples of a certain integer. We can prove this as follows. Every module must have some positive members; let d be the smallest such member and suppose that n is any other positive member. Then in fact d will divide n, for if it did not we would have a remainder so that $d=nz+c$, where c is less than d but positive. However, since $c=d-nz$ it follows that c is a member of the module which is positive, and less than d, contrary to our assumption. Thus every module, as we said, is a set of multiples of some basic number d. It is then natural to ask, what is the d for a module of the form $px+qy$? Evidently since x and y belong to the module, d must divide them both, so that if we write (x, y) for the highest common factor of x and y we must have $d \leqslant (x, y)$. However, the highest common factor divides both x and y and therefore divides every element of the module, i.e. in particular divides d. These two results together mean that d has to be the highest common factor of x and y. As a special case of this result it follows that, if two numbers x and y have 1 as their highest common factor, there are integers p and q such that $px+qy=1$.

We are now able to complete the proof of Euclid's first theorem. Here we are supposing that a prime, say p, divides a product ab and we have to show that p divides one of these factors, at least. Suppose that p does not divide a, so that a and p have the highest common factor 1. From what we have just proved this means that we can find integers r, s, such that

$$ra+sp=1.$$

However, it follows at once from this equation, by multiplication by b, that

$$rab+spb=b.$$

Evidently the prime p divides the left-hand side and therefore must divide b, which proves Euclid's theorem. It is now an easy matter to prove the fundamental theorem of arithmetic, that the decomposition into primes is unique. If this theorem were false it would mean that a number could split up into primes in two ways, and in one of these ways some prime, say p, must occur more times on one side than on the other. Let us cancel all the occurrences of the prime in the number in which it occurs least, so that we have an equation of the form $pq=r$, where r is a product of primes, say $r=abc$ . . ., and none of these primes is p. Evidently p divides the right-hand side, and so from Euclid's first theorem it must divide one of the factors on the right-hand side. But these factors are all primes, and so it can only divide one of them if it is equal to it, contrary to our assumption that the right-hand side did not involve p.

We can now return to the question of the diagonal of the unit square. If the diagonal, when written as a fraction in its lowest terms, is expressible in the form p/q, we have, by the theorem of Pythagoras, that $p^2=2q^2$. Now, from above, the product of p with itself can only be even if p is even, and so we may put $p=2r$.

However, this has the result that

$$q^2=2r^2,$$

so that by the same argument q is even. This implies that the original fraction was not after all in its lowest terms, and we have a contradiction. The kind of difficulty to which this gives rise can be seen from the reaction to it of the circle grouped around Pythagoras himself. Pythagoras is thought to have proved his well-known theorem on the right-angled triangle originally by means of similar triangles, and he would have set up the theory of similar triangles by means of an argument which assumed that any two magnitudes had a ratio which could be written as the ratio of two integers. When the fallacy in the proof of the theorem on the right-angled triangle became apparent to the Pythagoreans, they used the secret nature of their society to keep it concealed as long as possible.

Eventually the crisis became public property, and the shock galvanised the Greek mathematicians into a further brilliant achievement—the theory of proportions, which is set out at length in Euclid's "Elements". The theory of proportions would have enabled the Greeks to define an irrational number and work out the corresponding arithmetic, but perhaps because of their inadequate notation for numbers, they did not manage this.

At about the same time as these difficulties serious paradoxes arose in certain Greek mathematical theories of which we have only indirect evidence at present. The reason for this is interesting; so successful were these paradoxes that they appeared to have demolished completely the theories which they were criticising. These theories can be described collectively as theories of the *actual infinite*. The distinction we are making here between these theories and those of the potential infinite is already exemplified by two interpretations of the proposition (proved in one form by Euclid) "There is an infinity of primes". Euclid proves this result, the reader may remember, by supposing that P_n is the last prime; the number

$$N = (2.3.5.7 \ldots P_n) + 1,$$

the product being over all the primes, is then not divisible by any of the existing primes. Either this number is itself prime, which proves the theorem, since it is evidently larger than any of the primes which go to make it up, or else it is a composite number which has a prime factor larger than any of those primes, which again proves the theorem. Thus Euclid's proof is really of the statement that, given *any* prime, I can find a larger one. Such a statement is better expressed by saying that the number of primes is *potentially* infinite. During the long history of mathematics from the Greeks to Cantor, only the potentially infinite was permitted.

The interpretation in terms of the actual infinite is to say: "There is a number, which is the number of primes, and this number is an infinite one". Clearly, whether this second statement is also true or not depends, amongst other things, on our theory of numbers and whether it is big enough to include such members.

We may mention here that although Euclid's proof shows that the number of primes is infinite it does not give any worth while information on the *number* of primes less than a certain integer. The number of primes less than x is usually denoted $\pi(x)$. The proof as we have given it simply shows that, as x becomes very large, so does $\pi(x)$. It is possible to extend the proof of Euclid's theorem a little so as to produce a weak inequality for $\pi(x)$, or equivalently for the nth prime P_n. (N.B. $\pi(P_n) = n - 1$.)

It is evident that Euclid's proof has the form

$$P_{n+1} \leqslant 2.3 \ldots P_n + 1$$

so that if we can replace the product of primes by some more manageable expression, we can derive an inequality. One such is the theorem:

$$P_n < 2^{2^n}.$$

We may prove this by the process of *mathematical induction*; that is we show that the assumption that the result is true for one value of *n* and all lower ones implies that it is also true for the value one higher. If, then, we can show the result to be true for an initial value, say $n=1$, we can be sure it is true for all values (here, we have the *potential infinite*).

Let us suppose, then, that the result is true for all values of *n* up to $n=k$.

Then

$$P_{k+1} \leqslant P_1 P_2 P_3 \ldots P_k + 1$$
$$\leqslant 2^2 . 2^{2^2} . 2^{2^3} \ldots 2^{2^k} + 1$$
$$= 2^{(2+2^2+\ldots+2^k)} + 1.$$

Consider now

$$S = 2 + 2^2 + 2^3 + \ldots + 2^k;$$

then

$$2S = 2^2 + 2^3 + \ldots + 2^k + 2^{k+1},$$

so that

$$S = 2^{k+1} - 2,$$

and

$$P_{k+1} < 2^{2^{k+1}-2} + 1 < 2^{2^{k+1}}$$

This then extends the domain of truth up to $n=k+1$; moreover for $n=1$ we have $P_1=2$, $2^2=4$, so that the result is true for $n=1$ and so for all values of *n*.

Typical of the paradoxes of the actual infinite is the arrow of Zeno. The argument follows the following lines. Suppose that an arrow is fired from *A* to *B*. Before the arrow can reach *B* it must first reach a point half way between *A* and *B*—say B_1. Before it can reach B_1 it must reach a point half way between *A* and B_1—say B_2. Continuing in this way we have an infinity of points which the arrow must pass through before it can move at all. Because of the ideas that the Greeks had about infinity, this was held to require an infinite time, so that the conclusion was that the arrow really could not move at all. Although such a paradox is put in the form of impossibility of motion, it must surely be the case that motion, which everyone can see, survives the paradox, and the ideas of infinity which occur in the argument must be revised. In fact Archimedes was driven into the invention of the "Method of Exhaustion" to overcome such paradoxes.

The second crisis in the foundations of mathematics occurred at the beginning of the 19th century. In the 17th and 18th centuries mathematicians had been very struck by the power of the newly invented calculus, and had pushed on the solution of many problems which had hitherto been much too difficult for them. In so doing, they had failed to take proper account of the correctness or otherwise of their methods. In the hands of a genius like Euler for example, such a cavalier approach never got into trouble. Euler was able to employ in his analysis divergent series such as

$$1 - 1 + 1 - 1 + 1 - 1$$

which he then proceeded to sum by expressing it as the sum of a power series

$$1 - x + x^2 - x^3 + \ldots$$

when $x = 1$, and finding that this series has the value

$$\frac{1}{1 + x}$$

when x is less than 1, he concluded that the original series has the sum $1/(1 + 1)$, or $\frac{1}{2}$, when $x = 1$. As a matter of fact Euler was concerned with a practical problem and the solution of this practical problem was completed correctly by giving the value $\frac{1}{2}$ to the sum of the series. But of course there is no assurance that another practical problem might not throw up the sum series when a different value ought to be contributed to its sum, and indeed even with the same problem there is absolutely no assurance that the correct value will always appear for lesser mortals without Euler's physical intuition. For, of course, we have also

$$\frac{1 + x}{1 + x + x^2} = \frac{1 - x^2}{1 - x^3}$$
$$= (1 - x^2)(1 + x^3 + x^6 + \ldots) \quad \text{if } |x| < 1$$
$$= 1 - x^2 + x^3 - x^5 + x^6 - x^8 + \ldots$$

and Euler's trick will then give $\dfrac{1 + 1}{1 + 1 + 1} = \dfrac{2}{3}$ for the sum of the series. Moreover in some practical problems this may, indeed, be right for the sum of the series, so that no argument based on artificiality can get us out of trouble.

This second crisis was overcome by Cauchy in the 1830's. He showed that the mathematics which had been constructed in the previous century had been very irresponsible in its use of very small quantities, and he showed how to replace it by a careful use of a limiting procedure. It is true that, like most reformers, he went too far. There is no reason, for example, to reject Euler's method completely. It is much better to say that this method and a number of others are methods of summation which when applied to a convergent series give the sum which we usually attribute to that series and which sometimes give an answer when applied to a divergent series. The answer for a divergent series can then be defined as its sum under certain circumstances, and we can construct a perfectly good, interesting and useful mathematics of these sums. It is true that we cannot think of them as got by simply adding up all the terms but as a matter of fact neither ought we to think of the usual sum of a convergent series in this way. The only way in which we are not so well off as with a convergent series is that there is not a unique sum under all circumstances. Similarly there are various parts of mathematical analysis today which we believe to be perfectly satisfactory and which are of the greatest value in applications, but which would not have been satisfactory to Cauchy. However, they do not form a very large part of the whole of mathematics, so we may consider Cauchy's triumph as almost unblemished.

In the 60's and 70's of the last century Weierstrass and others carried on where Cauchy left off, and showed how everything could be reduced to a system constructed from the arithmetic of the positive integers. The irony of the situation is that this very careful work, meant to establish, beyond a shadow of doubt, the correctness and certainty of mathematics served only to reveal the pit over which it had been constructed. We shall describe in this chapter how the reduction can be done in more detail, but for the moment we can say simply that this construction of more complicated systems from elementary arithmetic relies on the existence of a theory of *sets*. The idea of a set is an intuitively obvious one; it is closely related to the usual use of the word "set", meaning a collection of things. However, the set theory required for Weierstrass and others is not only a theory of sets of integers. One must go on, as we shall see, and consider sets of these sets of integers, and sets of the sets of the sets, and so on. This continual reduction of the difficulties of mathematics to elementary arithmetic combined with set theory was so successful that Poincaré in 1900 claimed that mathematics had at last acquired a completely solid and sound basis. Fate determined that at the very moment when Poincaré made this extreme claim it had already turned out that the theory of infinite sets of integers was beset by very severe paradoxes, and certainly had no absolute security in its foundations. This was the beginning of the third crisis in mathematics, which is still with us at the present moment.

In this section we shall take the idea of a set for granted. The reader may think of it in the simplest intuitive terms as a collection of objects. Certainly this way of thinking about sets leads to trouble later, but before we can describe these problems it will be as well to see what advantages come from set theory. In this way we follow somewhat the same path as mathematicians followed historically. We shall consider in particular the uses of set theory in the foundations of arithmetic. It was during the 17th and 18th centuries that mathematics began to develop so quickly that mathematicians were forced to allow a temporary decline in their standards of exactness of argument, and to permit the introduction of irrational numbers and imaginary numbers without any proper basis. In the present section, however, we shall only accept the natural numbers, that is, the positive integers, as given to us intuitively, and shall seek to construct the rest of arithmetic. We do not mean to imply by this that there is nothing to be done in connexion with the foundations of the natural numbers; indeed the construction of these is one of the important topics of the next chapter. But for the present it will be sufficient to illustrate the importance of set theory in mathematics with the construction of the more complex part of arithmetic from the simpler part.

The use of a theory of sets is closely connected with the importance of relations. Let S be a set of objects

$$a, b, c, \ldots$$

We call R a relation on the set S if there exists a number n such that

$$Ra_1a_2 \ldots a_n \quad \text{where} \quad a_1, a_2, \ldots a_n \text{ belong to } S$$

is a proposition. This proposition may be put into words in the form that the particular elements of S which follow R in the statement of the proposition have the property described by the relation R. For example the set could be the set of integers. The relation R could be, for the case $n = 1$, the property of being prime. In that case

$$R2, R3, R5, R7 \ldots$$

would all be true propositions whilst

$$R4, R6, R8, R9 \ldots$$

would be false ones. Such a relation will be called a 1-term relation, or a predicate. If $n=2$, we would have a 2-term relation, or binary relation, of which an example for the set of integers is the relation "greater than". For this relation

$$R_{3,\,2}$$

is a true proposition, whereas

$$R_{2,\,3}$$

is a false one. An example for $n=3$ is provided by the relation of "betweenness" on the set of integers, the statement

$$Rabc$$

signifying that b lies between a and c, so that

$$R_{1,\,2,\,3}$$

is a true proposition and

$$R_{1,\,3,\,2}$$

is a false one.

A word is appropriate here about the commas that enter into the expression of relations in our example. We used none in the general theory, writing, for instance, $Rabc$. Unfortunately, once we come into contact with the integers we are in conflict with a different convention, that of place-value for Arabic numerals. R23 might be a two-place relation between 2 and 3 or it might be a predicate of 23. For this reason we modify the notation by means of commas.

Relations for higher values of n occur much less commonly, and we shall be particularly concerned here only with binary relations, so it is appropriate here to mention certain special kinds of relations of this sort. The first particular kind of binary relation to be considered is the transitive one. This relation is one like the "greater than" relation in the example above in which, whenever we have both

$$Rx,\,u \quad \text{and} \quad Ru,\,y,$$

we also have

$$Rx,\,y.$$

Other transitive relations on the integers are "less than" and "equals". The second particular kind of relation is the "reflexive".

This is a relation of the form that for every member of the set, x say, we have

$$Rx, x.$$

An example of a reflexive relation on the integers is that of "less than or equal to". The relation "less than" is clearly not reflexive. A third special kind of relation is the symmetric one in which, whenever two members of S stand in the relation

$$Rx, y$$

then also

$$Ry, x.$$

An example of a symmetric relation on the integers is "equals". Another one is

$$Rx, y$$

where Rx, y means that the absolute value

$$|x-y|$$

is even.

Let us now consider in particular a relation which has all three of the properties described; that is, it is reflexive, symmetric, and transitive. A relation of this sort is usually called an equivalence relation. Amongst the integers such a relation is provided by equality. Other examples are $R_p mn$, holding whenever $|m-n|$ is divisible by a prime p. The importance of an equivalence relation on a set is that it automatically divides the set up into a family of *sub-sets* that is, to sets whose members are some (or possibly all) of the members of S, with the property that every element of S is one of these sub-sets, and no two different sub-sets have any elements in common. The definition of these sub-sets is that x and y belong to the same sub-set if and only if

$$Rxy$$

where R is the equivalence relation. If two sub-sets have an element in common so that we have

$$Rxy \quad \text{and} \quad Rxz,$$

we can deduce at once that

$$Rxy \quad \text{and} \quad Rzx,$$

from which it follows that

$$Ryz$$

for any two elements of two sub-sets. This implies that the two sub-sets completely coincide. It is clear that every element belongs to one set, because of the reflexive nature of the relation. The family of sets contained in S will be said to be introduced by a "definition by abstraction" from the relation R.

For example consider the relation $R_2xy =$ "$|x-y|$ is divisible by 2" (i.e. even). There are two sub-sets, or *equivalence classes*, the even integers and the odd integers; every integer is either odd or even, and none is both.

We could, if we wish, define operations of addition and multiplication between the two sets E, O produced by this definition. For example, since, if x is in E and y is in O, $x+y$ is in O and xy is in E (whatever members of E, O are chosen) we have two tables:

+	O	E		x	O	E
O	E	O		O	O	E
E	O	E		E	E	E

It is simple, however, to observe in this case that a typical member of E is zero, and of O is 1; the tables for O and 1 are:

+	1	0		x	1	0
1	2	1		1	1	0
0	1	0		0	0	0

which differ from a straight translation of the ones above only by both 2 and 0 replacing E.

Let us now see how this abstraction is useful in constructing the whole of arithmetic from elementary arithmetic (that is, the positive integers only). So long as we have only positive integers we can always add and multiply, but reversing these procedures is only true under special conditions. For example, $a-b$ belongs to S only if $a>b$. We have somehow, for convenience, to embed S in a larger set which will contain also what we think of as the negative integers. We first consider the new set S to be that of all ordered pairs of positive integers, any one of which we can write in the form

$$(a, b).$$

(We can, between ourselves, think of this ordered pair as meaning the positive or negative integer

$$a-b$$

if it is helpful to do so. However, we must not of course use this fact in our proof since, so far, only the positive integers have been defined.) We next define an equivalence relation on the set S. We want this equivalence relation to be the same as equality applied to the positive and negative integers, so that we want

$$R((a, b), (c, d))$$

to mean what we would normally write as

$$a-b=c-d.$$

Since this statement would normally be equivalent to

$$a+d=b+c$$

we can take this new form, which involves only positive integers, as a *definition* of the relation R. The reader should verify that this relation is indeed reflexive, symmetric, and transitive remembering in his proof that he must not go outside the set of positive integers! This relation will therefore divide the set S of ordered pairs into equivalence classes, and all the members of one class will have the *same* meaning according to our interpretation of

$$(a, b)$$

as

$$a-b.$$

We can call these equivalence classes the *integers* meaning here positive and negative integers.

We can then define addition and multiplication of these integers by the rules

$$(a, b)+(c, d)=(a+c, b+d).$$

The reader should verify that these rules give the usual rules for operating with positive or negative integers. In this new system there is an equivalence class of which one member is

$$(\text{1, 1})$$

which corresponds in our interpretation to the integer zero. Moreover all the pairs of the form

$$(a+k, k)$$

which belong to the equivalence class of which one member is

$$(a+1, 1)$$

describe a member of S which behaves in exactly the same way as the positive integer a. We would like to say that the system of positive integers is included as a part of the new system. This is not quite true, since the new system consists of pairs of integers, but we can say that the new system contains a part which has exactly the same structure as the old system had.

Having constructed the positive and negative integers we can now always reverse the operation of addition of integers, and so carry out subtraction. The next problem is multiplication, and in order to be able to reverse this we need to construct the rational numbers. We now take our set S to be that of all ordered pairs of integers (where, now and later, "integer" will mean positive or negative integer or zero). Following the same lines as before, the pair (a, b) is to be interpreted as a/b, but we must not use the interpretation in our proofs. We must, however, restrict ourselves a little for this interpretation to be possible and take only the set of pairs (a, b) with $b \neq 0$. Let us notice, in passing, that the integers are already defined as sets, viz. equivalence classes, so that we have here a *set of ordered pairs of sets*, and we have now to define equivalence classes in *this* new set. To do this we define a relation R in S according to the rule

$$R((a, b), (c, d)) \quad \text{whenever} \quad ad = bc.$$

The reader will spot at once that when the ordered pairs have the interpretation stated, the relation R corresponds to equality between the ratios. He may also verify that the relation is reflexive, symmetric and transitive, and therefore defines a set of equivalence classes in S called the rational numbers. We can denote the class containing

$$(a, b)$$

by the notation

$$a/b.$$

The sum and product of rational numbers can then be defined in the usual way.

The discovery made by the Greeks was that even in the system of rational numbers certain operations are impossible. For example, there is no solution of the equation (for the diagonal of the unit square)

$$x^2 = 2.$$

The difficulties which one gets over by extending the set of positive integers to the whole set of integers, and then to the rational numbers, are all difficulties which could be put into much the same form, with certain equations which are insoluble with the old set of numbers and become soluble with the new. It is therefore natural to try to make another extension of the system of rational numbers, so that equations of this type become soluble. The process which we have used twice already cannot, as it happens, be used again to solve this problem, and we have to make a different use of the theory of relations. More than one way has been worked out of doing this, and the one which we shall pursue is that in terms of ordering relations.

We consider an ordering relation (which is actually that of "less than or equal to") which satisfies the assumptions

$$Raa$$

$$[Rab \text{ and } Rba] \text{ implies } a = b$$

We can imagine this ordering relation defined amongst the positive integers, and then we can define a corresponding order amongst *all* the integers by the rule "$R(a, b)(c, d)$ means $Ra+d, b+c$". Similarly the ordering relation may be extended to the rationals by defining $R\dfrac{a}{b}\dfrac{c}{d}$ to mean $R[(ad-bc)bd, 0]$. We have of course to verify that these definitions leave the above assumptions unchanged. It is also useful to consider a closely related ordering relation which we shall denote by $R^\star$ where $R^\star ab$ means that Rab and $a \neq b$. (This relation is, of course, simply the one usually called "less than".)

When we have constructed the ordering relation for the rational numbers we find that it differs from the ordering relation that we started with by an important property; that is, that it is *dense*. This means that, if a and b are any two rational numbers and $R^\star ab$, there is another rational number, c, such that both $R^\star ac$ and $R^\star cb$. At first this sounds like a way of saying that, when we have a dense ordering, there are no gaps in the set, but this is not the case at all. All that is stated by the denseness is that between any two numbers there will be a third one. If we consider the following sets of rationals (i) all negative rationals and those positive ones for which $R^\star x^2 2$ (i.e. $x^2 < 2$), (ii) all positive rationals also satisfying $R^\star 2x^2$ (i.e. $2 < x^2$), it is obvious that every rational number is contained in one of these two sets, and only in one. It seems as if the two sets touch without a gap, and also without any overlap. In fact, however, there is something missing, for there is no rational number whose square is two which would correspond to the place where the two sets touched.

In order to put this right, we talk in terms of pairs of sets of rational numbers. Such a pair (A, B) satisfies the following conditions,

(i) every rational is in one and only one of the two sets,

(ii) neither set is empty,

(iii) if we take any element of the set a there are always elements of a which are less than the element chosen, and, similarly, for the set b, and any particular element, there are always greater elements. Such a pair of sets is called a cut, and we define a relation in the set of cuts in the following way: $E((A, B)(C, D))$, means that there is at most one rational number which is either both in A and D or both in B and C. We leave it to the reader to verify that this relation is an equivalence relation, and therefore divides the set of cuts into equivalence classes. We have, then, again a definition by abstraction giving us this time the real numbers.

From what has been said in the preceding sections it is clear that the whole process of reduction of arithmetic (and other parts of mathematics likewise) to the system of positive integers, leans very heavily on the idea of a set. It is now time to see how Cantor went about the problem of constructing a set theory. Nowadays Cantor's set theory is usually called naïve set theory, but this uncomplimentary adjective is only applied as a result of hindsight. At the time the theory appeared deceptively simple and straightforward.

So long as we are considering only a finite number of things we can think of the *set* of the things as simply a collection of all of them. When we come to consider infinite sets, however, this is no longer possible. We can see what is really wanted by looking at the way in which the idea of an infinite set is used in the previous working. The members of a set are defined by having a certain property in common, so that the idea of a set and the idea of a property are roughly the same. The set consists of those objects which have the property in question. We can introduce a little notation to express these things more conveniently. We use $P(x)$ to denote some particular property; for example, if x is an integer, P might denote the property of being even, or of being prime. In the first case $P(2)$, $P(4)$, $P(6)$ . . . are true statements and $P(1)$, $P(3)$, $P(5)$ . . . are false ones. The corresponding sets will be denoted by $\hat{x}P(x)$, so that in the two cases considered this notation means the set of even integers or of primes. We speak of an integer *belonging* to one of these sets so that, when it belongs to the set of even integers, this is the same as saying that it is even. The symbol for "belonging to" is ε, so that we can write $y\varepsilon\hat{x}P(x)$, and we simply mean by this that y has the property which defines the set on the right-hand side; that is $P(y)$. It is tempting at this point to define a set as anything constructed in this way by means of a property. This definition involves the so-called "axiom of comprehension", that all such things constructed in this way may may be admitted as "respectable" sets in our set theory. No-one would have doubted this if things had not gone wrong.

Let us now consider the difficulties which Cantor's set theory gets into. The first paradox we will consider is due to Russell. It is convenient, as well as considering the set $\hat{x}P(x)$ which consists of the objects which have a certain property, to consider the objects which do not have the property. Thus if P is the property of being even, and we limit ourselves to the integers, the corresponding property is that of being odd. The negative of any given property P will be denoted by $\sim P$, so that, if P is the property of being even $\hat{x}[\sim P(x)]$ denotes the set of odd integers, and the true propositions are now $\sim P(1)$, $\sim P(3)$, $\sim P(5)$ and so on. Consider now the set R (for Russell) defined by $R=\hat{x}[\sim(x\varepsilon x)]$. We notice that R is a set of sets. There is of course nothing surprising in having to consider sets of sets; even in our construction of arithmetic from elementary arithmetic we had to define the various numbers in terms of those constructed already as sets, and so had to consider sets of sets. The defining property for Russell's set is whether or not the set x belongs to itself, and in Cantor's theory this was a perfectly reasonable question to ask. The set of all sets, being a set, belongs to the set of all sets; that is, itself; whereas a set of integers is not an integer but a set, and therefore does not belong to itself. It is natural to ask whether the set R belongs to itself or not. If R belongs to itself, then it satisfies the property $R\varepsilon R$, and so does not satisfy the negative of this property which occurs in the definition of R;

that is, it does not belong to itself. On the other hand if we assume that R does not belong to itself, this means that it does satisfy the defining relation for R, and so does belong to itself. In either case a severe contradiction has arisen.

This contradiction was not the first of those found in set theory, but it is one of the clearest, and occurs at a very early stage in the theory. A number of other paradoxes have been found, of which we have only space to describe a few. First consider the paradox, known to Cantor himself, of the largest cardinal number. In order to expound this properly, we ought to consider how the cardinal numbers of infinite sets may be compared. The cardinal number of a finite set is simply the number of members in it. This definition will not serve for infinite sets, but merely because the definition breaks down, it is not at all obvious that all infinite cardinals cannot be compared with each other. The cardinal of the set of rationals is in a fairly obvious way to be defined as the same as that of the set of integers. This is because we can arrange the rational numbers by some such rule as the following:

$$\frac{1}{1}, \frac{2}{1}, \frac{1}{2}, \frac{3}{1}, \frac{2}{2}, \frac{1}{3}, \frac{4}{1}, \frac{3}{2}, \frac{2}{3}, \frac{1}{4} \cdots$$

and number off the terms in this sequence with the integers so that to every integer there corresponds a unique rational number, and to every rational number (not necessarily in its lowest terms) corresponds a unique integer.

Are there any sets which have more members than the integers? Here again what we call "having more members" is a matter for definition, but we naturally wish the definition to agree as closely as possible with the normal meaning of the words. We can answer this question in the affirmative by pointing to the set of all real numbers. We defined the real numbers above by means of cuts, but in the present example we would prefer to use what is known to be an equivalent definition in terms of all infinite decimals. Consider the set of all infinite decimals between 0 and 1. Amongst these decimals there will of course be some which terminate and these correspond to the rational numbers. There will also be recurring decimals and these also correspond to rational numbers, whose denominators are 3, 6, 7 or 9. More generally we could consider other numbers which were defined as the solutions of algebraic equations of some degree. For example, the equation

$$x^5 + x - 1 = 0$$

has a solution between 0 and 1 and we can calculate its value to as many decimal places as we wish but we cannot express it in terms of square roots or higher roots. Lastly, there will be amongst these irrational numbers those which cannot be expressed as the solution of any algebraic equation. These are the numbers known as transcendental. We should not imagine that the successive categories of numbers refer to rarer and rarer occurrences. We are going to show below that there are many more irrational numbers than rational ones, so that in an obvious sense almost all the real numbers are irrational. Indeed although the existence of trasncendental numbers is not obvious, and for example such numbers as $\pi/4$ might well have turned out to be expressible in terms of square roots and so on, it is in fact the case that almost all numbers (in the same sense of almost all as before) are transcendental.

The question of whether a number is rational or not often occurs in mathematical problems which at first appear to have little relation to arithmetic. The Greeks attached a great deal of interest to the problem of squaring the circle, that is of constructing by means of ruler and compass alone a square equal in area to a given circle. They were unsuccessful in this project. The reason is that by means of ruler and compass alone one can construct only numbers which are expressible in terms of rational numbers by nothing worse than taking a square root. In order to show that the circle cannot be squared one has to prove that π is a number which is not expressible in this way in terms of rationals. In fact Lindemann showed in 1882 that π cannot be specified as the solution of *any* algebraic equation, that is, it is transcendental. This shows the impossibility of squaring the circle as a by-product. In view of the relative frequency of irrational numbers, and indeed of transcendental ones, one should not be surprised if a piece of working finishes up with an answer involving such numbers. One is only surprised at this because of the subtle influence of examination questions in which the setter has arranged matters to avoid irrational expressions. On the other hand it is worth remembering that all experimental results in science and all numbers actually used in calculations are rational numbers because we must always work to a certain number of decimal places and when we cut off an infinite decimal in this way we turn it into a rational number.

Let us return to our problem of showing that there are more real numbers between 0 and 1 than rational numbers. We represented these numbers by infinite decimals. There are others such as $\sqrt{2}$

which do not recur in any obvious manner but for which we have a simple rule for calculation (the rule being in this case the one involved in the usual longhand of the square root). Let us suppose that there is a numbering off of these decimals by means of the integers in the same way as we have just shown there exists for the rational numbers. We suppose the decimals to be written out according to this numbering in the following way:

$$\cdot a_1 a_2 a_3$$
$$\cdot b_1 b_2 b_3$$
$$\cdot c_1 c_2 c_3 \cdot \cdot \cdot$$

If this numbering process is satisfactory it must include all the infinite decimals 0 and 1. Now we can define a new number which we write in the form

$$\cdot \bar{a}_1 \bar{b}_2 \bar{c}_3 \cdot \cdot \cdot$$

where the bars over the various letters denote that the corresponding integer has been increased by 1 if it lies between 0 and 8, and is zero if the original integer is 9. This new number differs from the first one in our list in the first decimal place, from the second one in the second decimal place, and so on, so that it differs in one place at least from every member of the list. Our assumption that we could arrange all the numbers in order is therefore contradicted. In such a circumstance it is natural to say that the cardinal number of the set of infinite decimals is *larger* than that of the integers.

When we consider a finite set of cardinal n, there are various sub-sets of this set. The number of these sub-sets can be worked out as follows: there is one sub-set which actually consists of the whole set, there are n sub-sets with one member omitted, $\frac{1}{2}n(n-1)$ with two members omitted, and so on. If we include—as is usually done—the null set, which has no numbers, as a sub-set of every set, the total number of sub-sets is 2^n, and this is always greater that the cardinal of the original set. Cantor was able to prove the corresponding result for infinite sets, only of course, "greater than" now means in the sense in which the number of real numbers is greater than the number of integers. But consider the set of *all* sets. Such a set must clearly have the largest cardinal of any. On the other hand, the set of all sub-sets of this set—by Cantor's result—must be even bigger, so that we again have a contradiction.

We may also mention one or two other paradoxes of set theory which are related to the previous two. The Grelling paradox has the form of a language difficulty, but this is only apparent. We can divide the adjectives in the English language into two sets as follows: (i) those which we may call autological, which describe themselves; for example "short", since this is a short word, (ii) those which we can call heterological, which do not describe themselves; for example "long", which is not a long word. The word "heterological" is of course an adjective, and the question is whether it describes itself or not. If we suppose that it does, this means that it is heterological, and it therefore belongs to the set of adjectives which do not describe themselves. On the other hand, if we suppose that it does not describe itself, it is therefore by definition heterological, which is to say that it does describe itself. In either case we have a contradiction.

Another paradox which is connected with the last one is derived by considering the names of numbers in the English language; for example *five, one hundred, two hundred and seventy three* and so on. Each of these names contains a certain number of words. For example the first number requiring at least two words to describe it is 21 (making here the convention that hyphenated words count as two). The reader may work out for himself the first number which requires three words and the first which requires four. We now define a number as follows: "The first number whose definition needs at least eleven words". This definition is a perfectly good description of the number in question, but it contains only ten words, which is in contradiction to the definition of the number.

The occurrence of these paradoxes and other more technical ones made the reconstruction of set theory absolutely essential at the turn of the century.

Examples

1. Explain why the following dilemma is not a serious paradox for the logician and mathematician: An Eastern ruler ordains that the shaving of the inhabitants of a certain village shall be regulated as follows: any male who does not shave himself shall be shaved by the barber, and the barber is forbidden, under pain of death, from shaving anyone who is in the habit of shaving himself. Who shaves the barber?

2. Explain how the fact that there are more reals than rationals is a particular case of Cantor's theorem about sub-sets.

5 PRINCIPIA MATHEMATICA

THE APPROACH of modern workers in logic to the problems considered by Boole and Aristotle is a completely different one from theirs. Aristotle, and Boole following him, analysed everything in terms of a particular form of proposition; that is, the subject-predicate form. As we said above, this is really begging the whole question, since the greatest difficulties in analysing argument lie in reducing it to this form. Once the reduction has been carried out everything is relatively straightforward. The modern developments consider propositions in general, without making any specific assumptions about the form of a proposition. All that is required is that a statement, to be a proposition, must be either true or false; one is not allowed to include, amongst propositions, meaningless or ambiguous statements. It is clear that logic must therefore take a more abstract form. The conclusions in Aristotle's scheme followed because certain terms (the subject, the predicate and the middle term) occurred in certain ways in the premises. Here we have to make decisions about arguments without using such information. Logic then simply discusses how we can derive new propositions from old ones; that is, given some propositions as the beginning of an argument, it discusses the general process of reaching another proposition regarded as its conclusion.

Before we take up in detail the way in which this is done, it is as well to notice that, although Boole and Aristotle confined themselves to a very special form of proposition, within this self-appointed restriction they were very successful. Each of them was able to give what we now would call a 'decision procedure' for the systems involved. In Aristotle's case a syllogism was valid if, and only if, it was in conformity with the rules of the syllogism (Chapter 2, Example 1). The decision procedure for Boole's system is not very different in Boole's original version, but with the simplified version given here it is much easier; an argument is valid if, and only if, it falls into one of the two forms described in Chapter 3. We shall find that the existence of a decision procedure plays an important part in what follows. It is the existence of such a procedure which leads to the essential triviality of the systems. When a decision procedure is known, there is no longer any scope for art and ingenuity in the system; everything can be decided by a mechanised procedure—given long enough.

When we come to elaborate logic in the more modern fashion, we shall find that it exhibits clearly the point in its development at which a decision procedure ceases to hold. In the early stages we shall have a pseudo-algebraic structure analogous to Boole's, and we shall show (a rather more difficult task than with Boole's system) that there is a decision procedure for this system. Thus these early stages partake of exactly the same kind of triviality as Aristotle's and Boole's structures. It is worth considering them in detail, however, because they serve to exhibit this particular triviality (which is not always easy to see) in a clear manner; when we have examined closely a system with a decision procedure we are in a much better position to understand what it is like for another system to have none. (Moreover we must, of course, begin at the beginning before we can construct the more elaborate systems.)

As soon as we generalise our structure—as we must if it is to be adequate even for elementary arithmetic—we reach a system for which a decision procedure no longer holds. Now there is scope for ingenuity in proof, but it remains an open question whether the new system is actually a *decidable one* in the sense that every proposition in it can either be proved true from the axioms, or can be proved false from the axioms. The property of being decidable is of course a weaker one than having a decision procedure. It is quite possible to imagine a system in which every proposition has a proof or disproof, but in which there is no uniform procedure for discovering proofs, so that skill and ingenuity are essential. Until 1930 many people supposed mathematics to be such a system, but the aim of this book is to explain how this is not so. There is no decision procedure in mathematics because, in fact, there are always propositions which cannot be decided from any particular set of axioms. We shall find in later chapters that as soon as our system is adequate for the description of elementary arithmetic, it ceases to be decidable.

This chapter is devoted to the system of logic put forward by A. N. Whitehead and Bertrand Russell in their "Principia Mathematica", published in Cambridge from 1910 onwards. Whitehead and Russell were seriously disturbed by the situation described in the last chapter: that major paradoxes had arisen in mathematics. They felt that the way of avoiding such a scandalous situation was to base mathematics on some more secure foundation, and their choice of such a foundation was obviously very restricted. They came to the conclusion that logic would serve as a secure basis for mathematics—a conclusion very understandable in the particular intellectual atmosphere in Cambridge in the early part of this century. They soon found, however, that logic, meaning by this word, the subject developed by the philosophers for about 2,000 years, was in fact in a very inadequate state. They therefore had to start from scratch, and construct it as they went.

As we said in the last paragraph, the essential feature of these new developments is that propositions of any form are admitted. Accordingly we shall denote propositions by neutral letters like p, q, and r which do not suggest to the mind anything about their structure. We shall begin our study in an intuitive manner, by exploiting to the utmost the requirement that propositions must be true or false. Later we shall return to the beginning and explain something of how Whitehead and Russell chose to begin the subject; their way is consistent with the present one, although it is rather different in appearance. Every proposition, then, is either true or false, and accordingly we can associate with each proposition one of two *values*. It is convenient to use the two numbers o and 1 for the values false and true, and, if we denote the value of a proposition p by $|p|$, the statement "p is true" is equivalent to $|p|=1$, and "p is false" is equivalent to $|p|=$o. The fact that we are using the numbers o and 1 as a convenient notation at this point does not imply that we are going to perform ordinary arithmetic with them. In particular rational numbers between o and 1 will have no meaning; neither will numbers greater than 1. On the other hand we are at liberty *if we wish* to perform arithmetical operations with the numbers representing the values of our propositions, and we may notice that if $|p|=x$, we have—no matter whether p is true or false —that $x^2=x$. The occurrence of this equation reminds us strongly of Boole's system.

We now have to consider how to derive other propositions from the one given already. Since now we have no interest in the structure or content of propositions, but only in whether they are true or false, it follows that our new propositions must depend, as to whether or not they are true, only on the truth or falsehood of the old ones. The first obvious case of this is when we have the negative of a certain proposition; that is, the proposition which is false if p is true, and true if p is false. We usually denote this proposition by $\sim p$, so that we can write $|\sim p| = 1 - |p|$. Instead of writing an algebraic formula we can equally well put it in the form of a table like this

p	$\sim p$
0	1
1	0

This tabulation is useful in what follows, because the algebraic expression is not always so obvious.

Next we wish to consider how to associate new propositions with *pairs* of old ones. The association which is introduced first by Whitehead and Russell is called "alternation", and corresponds fairly closely to the word "or" in ordinary English. We denote the new proposition, "p or q", by $p \vee q$, but we must notice here that we are to mean by this that either p or q or both of them are true. If we wish to consider the case when either p or q—but not both—are true, we can easily construct it from the propositions which we are describing here. The table $p \vee q$ is evidently of the form

$p \backslash q$	0	1
0	0	1
1	1	1

and a little experiment will enable the reader to derive the corresponding algebraic form

$$|p \vee q| = |p| + |q| - |p||q|.$$

Other operations between propositions which yield new propositions are $p \,\&\, q = \sim(\sim p \vee \sim q)$ and $p \to q = (\sim p) \vee q$. The reader should work out the table for each of these operations, and show that the first of them agrees with the usage in ordinary language.

The second one is often rendered as "implies". However, this is a short description of it which is rather inaccurate, since the proposition is always true so long as every p is false or q is true. In other words, it is true—no matter what the conclusion q—so long as p is false. This is not exactly what is meant by implication in normal usage, where the word carries some suggestion that q is true *as a result of p*. In normal usuage "If it is raining now, the pitch will be too wet for play" is regarded as a more reasonable inference than "If wishes are horses then $2+2=5$". But the distinction between them depends on their subject-matter and so is beyond our means to discuss in the system. We must accept or reject both of them. We can avoid some of the appearance of paradox by rendering $p \rightarrow q$ in words as "If p then q".

The various operations discussed here do not have to be all defined independently. The important thing is that for any truth-values of p and q the truth-value of a combined proposition must be determined. There are as many combinations of p and q as there are tables with four entries, each of which is either 0 or 1; that is, 16. These 16 are not of course all equally important. If all the entries are 0, we have a combination which is always a false proposition, and if all the entries are 1, we have a proposition which is always true, irrespective of the truth-values of p and q. Such combinations are not "genuine" combinations of p and q, since they do not depend on p and q at all. In the same way other tables can be disregarded; for example, those in which both rows are the same, or both columns are the same. The reader may like to work out how many tables there are left if these have been struck out, and he may classify these tables into sets by choosing one such table and seeing all the others which can be got from it by the following process:

    (a) interchanging p and q,
    (b) interchanging p and its negative,
    (c) turning the combined proposition into its negative.

Another question which may occur to the reader is whether he can construct combinations of propositions from a small number of assumed combinations which will give all the tables which can be written down. There are two problems here: firstly, given some initial tables, to construct others; secondly, to determine which initial tables are adequate for this construction. We shall not tackle the second of these problems in any detail, but confine ourselves to the first in two particular cases. Firstly suppose that, in keeping with "Principia Mathematica", we take as our basic operations $\sim p$ and $p \vee q$. If we are given these operations, we can construct, from the definitions given above, p & q and $p \rightarrow q$. Suppose now that any particular table is given to be constructed by means of these basic operations. For example, consider the table

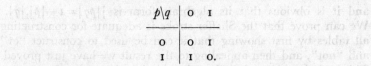

$p\backslash q$	0	1
0	0	1
1	1	0.

The following method will always give an answer, though it may be possible in some cases to find the answer more quickly. One simply looks at the cases which make the combined propositions true, and writes down (with the interpretation of $\sim$, v, and & described) the instances in logical notation. Thus, for the table cited, when we have one or other but not both p & q false we write

$$(\sim p \text{ \& } q) \text{v} (p \text{ \& } \sim q).$$

In this expression the contents of the two brackets can then be expressed in terms of the original operations according to the definitions. In doing so it will be useful to notice that $|\sim\sim p| = |p|$ for any p, so that $\sim\sim p$ may always be replaced by p. Accordingly our expression is, since

$$p \text{ \& } q = \sim(\sim p \text{v} \sim q),$$
$$[\sim(p\text{v}\sim q)]\text{v}[\sim(\sim p\text{v}q)].$$

Similarly for the table

$p\backslash q$	0	1
0	1	0
1	1	1

we write down

$$\sim q\text{v}p.$$

(It is, in fact, $q{\rightarrow}p$.)

It is clear then that the two operations "not" and "or" will suffice to construct any table, but the reader may wonder whether we cannot do even better and construct everything from a single operation. This is possible, and one way of doing it is to take as a new basic operation the *Sheffer stroke* defined by $|pq=\sim(p \text{ \& } q)$; that is, the proposition which is true so long as one or both of p and q is false. This has the table

$p\backslash q$	0	1
0	1	1
1	1	0

and it is obvious that its algebraic form is $||pq| = 1 - |p| \cdot |q|$. We can prove that the Sheffer stroke is adequate for constructing all tables by first showing that it can be used to construct "or" and "not", and then appealing to the result we have just proved. This is obvious, since it is clear that $|pp$ has the same value as $\sim p$. Having constructed "not p" we can get from the original definition $|(\sim p)(\sim q)$ as an expression for "p or q", which can of course be written entirely in terms of the stroke in the form $||pp|qq$. The notation here needs a little explanation. Sheffer originally wrote his operation p/q, so that, if 3 letters are involved, brackets are needed to distinguish between $p|(q|r)$ and $(p|q)|r$. [The reader should confirm that such a distinction is indeed necessary, by proving that $|p|(q|r)| - |(p|q)|r| = |r| - |p|$.].

However by the simple trick of putting the stroke in front of the letters to which it applies we can (since we know that each stroke must apply to two propositions) always omit the brackets. Thus $|p|qr$ must mean $p|(q|r)$ in Sheffer's notation, whereas $||pqr$ means $(p|q)|r$.

The discussion above leant heavily on the idea of a truth-value of a proposition. This is a very convenient way to introduce logic, but it is a relatively recent approach, and that of Whitehead and Russell was quite different. They began with certain axioms about propositions and their combinations, the idea being that these combinations were *not* defined independently of the axioms by some verbal description (as we did in §2) but were given a meaning only in virtue of the axioms. The particular verbal description of §2 is then to be regarded as a particular interpretation of the axioms, but by no means the only one, nor necessarily the "correct" one.

The primitive ideas taken for granted in "Principia Mathematica" were ∨ and ∼. Whitehead and Russell then make the definitions

$$A: \quad p \to q = \sim p \vee q$$
$$B: \quad p \& q = \sim(\sim p \vee \sim q).$$

The axioms chosen are written:

1. $p \vee p \to p$

2. $q \to p \vee q$

3. $p \vee q \to q \vee p$

4. $p \vee (q \vee r) \to q \vee (p \vee r)$

5. $(q \to r) \to [(p \lor q) \to (p \lor r)]$.

From a set of axioms alone, of course, nothing follows automatically —we need to be given *rules of inference* to enable us to infer new propositions. There are two rules of inference in "Principia Mathematica":

(i) Substitution: for any proposition p in a compound proposition any other proposition (possibly a compound one) may be substituted, so long as *all* occurrences of p are substituted for.

(ii) *Modus ponens:* if a proposition A, and another one, $A \to B$, have both been proved, B is to be regarded as proved.
(Clearly *modus ponens* is what gives→the meaning we want it to have)

Let us now see how to carry out some of the proofs of some of the more elementary theorems in "Principia Mathematica". We start numbering these at 6 (since 1 . . . 5 are axioms, and therefore also to be assumed as theorems).

6. $(p \to \sim p) \to \sim p$.

(The reader should interpret this; it represents a special case of *reductio ab absurdum*.) We can present the steps of the proof as follows:

Proof: $p \xrightarrow{(1)} \sim p : (\sim p \lor \sim p) \to \sim p$

$q \xrightarrow{(A)} \sim p : (p \to \sim p) \to \sim p$.

Here the left-hand column consists of the instructions, respectively: "Substitute for p, $\sim p$, in axiom 1; then in definition A write $\sim p$ for q". We shall now give only the instructions on how to carry out the proof; the reader should fill in the corresponding right-hand column himself, and observe carefully how the proof follows.

7. $(p \to \sim q) \to (q \to \sim p)$

Proof: $p,q \xrightarrow{(3)} \sim p, \sim q$

$\xrightarrow{(A)}$

8. $[q \to r] \to [(p \to q) \to (p \to r)]$

(In the interpretation we have mentioned, this is one form of the syllogism.)

Proof: $p \xrightarrow{(5)} \sim p$

9. $p \rightarrow (p \vee p)$

Proof: $q \xrightarrow{(2)} p$.

10. $p \rightarrow p$ (the classical logician's "law of identity").

Proof: $r \xrightarrow{(8)} p$: ★

$q \xrightarrow{(*)} p \vee p$: ★★

By 1, 9 & *modus ponens* twice, result follows. [Here the structure of the proof is a little more complicated; we use ★ to denote the result of the instruction $r \xrightarrow{(8)} p$, and an operation is then performed on this result in the next line.] This is the first time that we have used *modus ponens* so it will be as well to write out the whole proof:

$$\text{★ is } [q \rightarrow p] \rightarrow [(p \rightarrow q) \rightarrow (p \rightarrow p)].$$

We notice here that the left-hand side is $q \rightarrow p$, which is evidently *not* a theorem for any q at random, but since q is not in the final answer it may well be possible to make a special choice of q which will make $q \rightarrow p$ a theorem and so enable us to use *modus ponens*. In casting about for such a q, however, we should keep an eye on the next stage, when we hope also to be able to deal with $p \rightarrow q$ by *modus ponens*. Axiom 1 and theorem 9 together suggest the right q to choose, viz. $p \vee p$. We then have ★★ which is

$$\underbrace{[p \vee p \rightarrow p]}_{A} \rightarrow [\underbrace{(p \rightarrow p \vee p)}_{B} \rightarrow \underbrace{(p \rightarrow p)}_{C}],$$

where A & B are already proved. One application of *modus ponens* gives $B \rightarrow C$, another C.

11. $\sim p \vee p$ (The classical logician's "law of excluded middle".)

Proof: 10 and A

12. $p \vee \sim p$

Proof: $\left. \begin{array}{l} p \xrightarrow{(3)} \sim p \\ q \longrightarrow p \end{array} \right\}$

Use 11.

13. $p \rightarrow (\sim\sim p)$

Proof: $p \xrightarrow{(12)} \sim p$

    Use A.

14. $p \lor \sim\sim\sim p$

Proof: $\left.\begin{array}{l} q \xrightarrow{(5)} \sim p \\ r \rightarrow \sim\sim\sim p \end{array}\right\} P \rightarrow (Q \rightarrow R)$ (say)

    $p \xrightarrow{(13)} \sim p$ P

    Use 12.

15. $(\sim\sim p) \rightarrow p$

Proof: $q \xrightarrow{(3)} \sim\sim\sim p$

    Use 14, and A.

16. $(\sim p) \lor (\sim q) \rightarrow \sim(p \,\&\, q)$

Proof: $p \xrightarrow{(13)} \sim p \lor \sim q$

    Use B.

17. $\sim(p \,\&\, \sim p)$ (The classical logician's "law of contradiction".)

Proof: $p \xrightarrow{(12)} \sim p$

    $q \xrightarrow{(16)} \sim p$.

Then use *modus ponens*

So we can go on, with successively more complicated compound propositions, and Whitehead and Russell do indeed elaborate their system at great length. Nowadays, however, because of the essential triviality of the system (notwithstanding the ingenuity which can easily be expended on the construction of proofs!) a short cut is possible, and this is described in the next section.

We define the truth-value of any compound proposition in terms of the truth-values of its constituents by the two tables (which we have had before)

p	$\sim p$
0	1
1	0 ,

$p \vee q$	0	1
0	0	1
1	1	1

Since every compound proposition can be made up from $\sim$ and $\vee$, this definition always gives a truth-value.

Examine, now, the axioms 1 to 5; the truth-value of 1 is

$$|p \vee p \rightarrow p| = |\sim(p \vee p) \vee p| = |\sim p \vee p| = 1$$

for *both* truth-values of p. Similarly for the other 4 axioms, as the reader may verify directly. (In the case of the more complicated ones it saves labour, instead of verifying each case in turn, to consult the table for $\rightarrow$ and argue on these lines (say, for Axiom 5): How can the truth-value be zero? Only if

$$|q \rightarrow r| = 1 \quad \text{and} \quad |(p \vee q) \rightarrow (p \vee r)| = 0.$$

This latter case, in turn, requires $|p \vee q| = 1$, $|p \vee r| = 0$, and the second of these means $|p| = |r| = 0$, so that $|q| = 1$. But now $|q \rightarrow r| = 0$, contrary to our original supposition; since we have reached a contradiction, no assigning of truth-values to p, q, r can possibly make the result zero.)

Compound propositions whose truth-values are always 1 are called *tautologies*; so we have proved that all the axioms are tautologies. But now consider the rules of inference; substitution in a tautology must evidently result in a new tautology. Moreover, if A & $A \rightarrow B$ are tautologies, the table for $\rightarrow$ means that $|B| = 1$, i.e. B is also a tautology. Hence the rules of inference, acting on tautologies, can give only tautologies. In other words, we have proved that *every theorem is a tautology*.

In recent years an interesting application has been made of these tables in the design of switching circuits. The connection is simply that the two values 0 and 1 which the variables may have in the mathematical system correspond to the two positions, open and closed, that an electrical switch can have. It is a matter of indifference which way round we identify the symbols but in this book we shall adhere to the convention that 0 represents an open switch (so that no current passes) and 1 represents a closed switch, passing current.

A particular electrical device which originally made the application of a complicated mathematical technique worthwhile was the
relay. A relay is simply a device which operates a switch according
to whether or not current is flowing in another circuit. The way
in which it does this is by employing an electro-magnet which draws
a piece of metal towards itself when current flows, this piece of
metal being used to operate contacts of a switch in a second circuit.
Depending on how one arranges the mechanical part of the relay
we may either employ it directly so that the second circuit has its
switch closed when current flows and open otherwise, or oppositely
so that the second circuit is an open circuit when the current flows
and conversely. We can then use a hand operated switch to inject
information into our circuit, and the current from this switch can

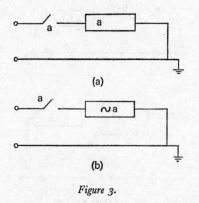

(a)

(b)

Figure 3.

then be used to work a relay or possibly several relays, transferring
the information we have put in, or its negative, to various switches.
We can represent this schematically in *Figure 3*, in which the left-
hand gap represents a manually closed switch and the box on the
right-hand side represents the relay. Of course another arrangement with the relay arranged in the opposite direction would
be that shown in *Figure 3b*.

When we have two switches these can be arranged, as all students
of electricity are well aware, either in series or in parallel. If the
switches are in series, current will only flow if both of them are

closed, whereas if they are in parallel it will flow if either of them
is closed. This arrangement can be summarised using the tables
for two of the logical connectives by *Figure 4*. [The reader
may easily verify that the table for the connective "and" is

$p \& q$	0	1
0	0	0
1	0	1	]

It is possible by means of the tables which we have constructed
already to devise quite complicated switching circuits. For example
there is the circuit known to engineers as the *lock-in circuit*. This

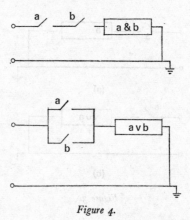

Figure 4.

circuit passes current when one switch is closed and continues to
pass current until another switch is operated. It then ceases to
pass current until the first switch is closed again. The reader may
exercise his ingenuity in determining how to make such a switch.
One solution is to be found in *Figure 5* where the two switches which
are hand operated are spring loaded, one to remain open unless
operated, the other to remain closed. The reader may care to verify
that the various switches satisfy the logical identity.

$$b \leftrightarrow a \ \& \ (b \lor c)$$

It is of particular interest to devise a circuit corresponding to the Sheffer stroke operation, since, as we know, any table can be constructed from the table for this operation. Since it is clear that the Sheffer stroke could have been defined by

$$|pq = \sim p \vee \sim q,$$

a circuit which constructs this operation is that shown in *Figure 6*.

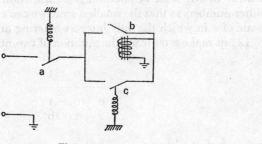

Figure 5.

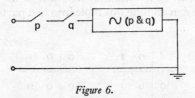

Figure 6.

In understanding some of the later work in this book it will be helpful to have in mind the use of these switching circuits in making computers. A computer can be built using relays, though modern large electrical machines employ other switching elements (valves or transistors) which behave in somewhat the same way. We shall confine our attention here to machines involving relays.

In order to deal with numbers it will be necessary to express them all in terms of the two symbols (0 and 1) which we have employed in these tables. At first this sounds rather a tall order, until we realise that the expression of numbers in our original notation is all carried out in terms of only 10 quantities (zero and the first 9 positive integers). The fact that 10 quantities are used is sometimes expressed by saying that we are working in the scale of 10, meaning by this that if we count upwards the number which occurs after 9 is obtained by returning to the initial value 0 again, and carrying 1 to the next column. A moment's consideration will convince the reader that other numbers instead of 10 can be employed as the basis of a scale of notation (and indeed a half-hearted attempt to use 12 is found in the English monetary system). The essential feature of any scale of notation is a distinction between 0 and the other numbers so that the smallest scale we can employ would be the scale of 2 in which the only integers entering are 0 and 1.

Let us make a table for the addition of two numbers in this scale:

+	0	1
0	0	1
1	1	10

The entries in this table are all quite evident except for the bottom right-hand one. This one represents the number, usually called 2, in this particular scale of notation. If we want to make a machine to add numbers we can analyse this table into two parts in the following way

A	0	1		B	0	1
0	0	1		0	0	0
1	1	0 ,		1	0	1 .

The second of these tables gives us the figure which has to be carried to the next column whilst (A) gives us the number to be written down in the column which we are adding. We can then easily devise a circuit which will add together two numbers, the output for this circuit consisting of a number to go in the same column and another one to be carried. One way of doing this can be seen in *Figure 7*. Such a circuit however is not yet quite complicated enough to be a basic circuit for an electrical adding machine because at the next stage we shall have to be able to add onto the two figures presented the quantity carried from the previous stage.

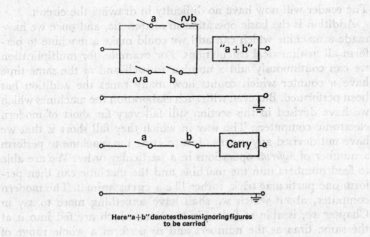

Here "a + b" denotes the sum ignoring figures
to be carried

Figure 7.

Accordingly the basic unit both for the figure in the same column and the carrying figure is one which will add together three quantities and not two. The easiest way of devising such a circuit is to tabulate first the work which we want it to do and such a table will have the following form:

a	b	Carried	Carry	Sum
0	0	0	0	0
0	0	1	0	1
0	1	0	0	1
0	1	1	1	0
1	0	0	0	1
1	0	1	1	0
1	1	0	1	0
1	1	1	1	1

It is very easy to see what circuit is required for the carrying figure since something must be carried if at least two of the three input figures is 1. For the sum we can write down by means of the method of paragraph 2

"Sum" $= (\sim a \ \& \ \sim b \ \& \ c) . \textbf{v} . (\sim a \ \& \ b \ \& \ \sim c)$
$$. \textbf{v} . (a \ \& \ \sim b \ \& \ \sim c) . \textbf{v} . (a \ \& \ b \ \& \ c).$$

The reader will now have no difficulty in drawing the circuit.

Addition is the basic operation in arithmetic, and once we have made a machine which can add we could make a machine to perform all arithmetical calculations. For example, for multiplication we can continuously add a number to itself and at the same time have a counter which counts how many times the addition has been performed. But even with such elaboration the machines which we have devised in this section still fall very far short of modern electronic computers. The way in which they fall short is that we have not devised any means of instructing the machine to perform a number of *different* operations in a particular order. We are able to feed numbers into the machine and the machine can then perform one particular trick, rather like a circus animal. The modern computer, about which we shall have something more to say in Chapter 10, is able to follow instructions which are fed into it at the same time as the numbers and so perform a whole range of arithmetical operations.

Examples

1. Define a *near-tautology* as a proposition A, involving a number of variables $p, q, \ldots$, such that the truth-value of A is 1 for all combinations except one of the truth-values of $p, q \ldots$

(i) p is a near-tautology.

(ii) $p \vee q$ is a near-tautology; what other 3 are there with two variables?

(iii) Show that there are near-tautologies with any number of variables.

(iv) If A is a near-tautology and B is a tautology, and all the variables in A occur in B, then $B \rightarrow A$ is a near-tautology.

2. Try to carry out the construction of a *three-valued logic* by the following device:

(i) A three-valued proposition P is a pair of ordinary propositions $P = (p_1, p_2)$. Define $|P| = |p_1| + |p_2|$, and call P false, undetermined or true according as $|P| = 0, 1$, or 2.

(ii) Prove that we do *not* get a 3-valued logic by defining $P \vee Q = (p_1 \vee q_1, p_2 \vee q_2)$.
(Hint: if $|P| = 1$, $|Q| = 1$, prove $|P \vee Q|$ may be either 1 or 2.)

(iii) Prove that $\sim P = (\sim p_1, \sim p_2)$ *is* a possible definition of $\sim P$.

(iv) Show, however, that the trick employed in (ii) will not work for any connective in the two-valued logic which is not trivial (trivial meaning that the value for a pair of propositions depends only on at most one member of the pair).

(v) Define $|PvQ| = \text{Min}\,(|p_1 v q_1| + |p_2 v q_2|)$ where the minimum is over possible p_i, q_i such that $|p_1| + |p_2| = |P|$, $|q_1| + |q_2| = |Q|$. Prove PvQ has the table

	0	1	2
0	0	1	2
1	1	1	2
2	2	2	2

(vi) Now define $P \to Q = (\sim P) v Q$ and calculate the table for $P \to Q$. [This is Kleene's "strong three-valued logic", constructed by him (by a different method) in 1938.]

6 THE DECISION PROBLEM

WE HAVE already discussed the notion of a decision procedure. The systems of Aristotle and Boole have decision procedures of a kind, but of course these systems have only a very narrow range of applicability. We have gone half-way towards constructing a decision procedure for the system of Whitehead and Russell, in this sense: Any statement in the system can only possibly be derived from the axioms (that is, be proved) if it is a tautology. Given any statement, then, whose provability we have to decide on, we investigate whether or not it is a tautology. If it is not, we can be quite sure that it is false, that is, cannot be derived from the axioms. We should have a complete decision procedure if only we could say something about the case when the statement *is* a tautology. In fact we can do this. We shall show later in this chapter that the converse result is also true; that is, that every tautology is a theorem.

This will be more difficult than the result at the end of the last chapter, since we shall have to show that, given a tautology, there actually is a derivation of it from the axioms. The most straightforward way of doing this is to give a rule which will enable us always to construct such a derivation. We shall not, in fact, tackle the problem of providing this rule for the system constructed by Whitehead and Russell. Such a rule can be constructed, but it is a rather complicated matter. We shall instead first construct a simpler system, due to Church, which is (i) completely equivalent to Whitehead and Russell's system (although this equivalence is rather difficult to prove, and we shall not attempt it here); (ii) self-evidently equivalent to the system of Whitehead and Russell with the interpretation given in the last chapter. (The second statement is of course different from and rather weaker than the first!) The conclusion of this chapter is, then, that the logic of "Principia Mathematica", and equivalently Church's system, is trivial in the same way as Boole's and Aristotle's logic, since we could make a machine which would decide the validity of every statement. On the other hand the triviality of, for example, Church's system, is by no means so obvious a matter as it was with Boole's and needs considerable ingenuity in its proof. By considering a system of this kind which has a decision procedure, although not an obvious one, we put ourselves in a much better position for understanding systems like the logic which is actually used in mathematical arguments, for which no decision procedure exists.

We shall now formulate Church's system. The idea behind this system is the following: we want to show that tautologies are all provable; that is, we want to show how to construct a proof of certain kinds of statement. There are of course an infinite number of statements that one can make if one places no restriction on the length of a statement (length meaning the number of symbols in it). It will only be possible to show that every one of an infinite class of statements is provable if we have some principle of *induction*, in the usual mathematical sense; that is, we shall want to assume that all formulae of a certain length are provable, and show that in this case formulae of the next longest length are also provable. We cannot employ this method directly with Whitehead and Russell's system because there are *two* basic connectives in the system, negation and alternation (even if we transcribe everything into the two that they begin with). Therefore the theorems of a certain length comprise many different kinds of statement. We need a system with one connective, and then we can count the length of a statement as the number of times which this connective occurs in it. From the last chapter the reader might jump to the conclusion that the Sheffer stroke is such a connective: this is true, but the stroke does not have an easily understood meaning. Church therefore hit upon a useful mathematical device which enabled him to use as his only connective the implication of Whitehead and Russell. This device was to introduce a *constant* proposition, f, which was always false. Thus f denotes in his system a proposition which differs from p, q, and r by the fact that, in any calculations of truth values, f is always to be given the value 0. Since there is only one connective, we can do one of two things: (a) we can write it in front of the letters to which it applies, and then we can do without brackets, (b) we can omit any sign for the connective at all (just as we do for multiplication in ordinary algebra) and then we shall have to use brackets to indicate the order in which the connectives are to be filled in. We shall take the second course of action because this is more in keeping with the spirit of Church's system, since it provides statements looking somewhat more like the "normal" representation of their meaning. The reader will find it instructive to re-write all our arguments using alternative (a).

In expounding Church's system we shall also become a little more formal than we have been, by stating all the symbols employed, and so on. One of the objects of the book is to work up to the idea of a formal system. The system of Whitehead and Russell is a formal system, but we have presented it in a somewhat informal manner because this is easier for the reader when he first meets such systems. In any formal system one encounters the following constituents:

(i) Certain constant symbols. For Church's system there are three in number: (,) and f.

(ii) An alphabet of variables, which we shall take here as $p, q, r, \ldots$

(iii) A set of rules, which state which strings of variables and constants constitute sensible statements; the so-called well-formed formulae. These rules are as follows for Church's system: (a) f is a well-formed formula. (b) Any variable is a well-formed formula. (c) If A and B are well-formed formulae, so also is AB.

(iv) A set of particular well-formed formulae, known as axioms, from which others known as theorems are to be deduced. The axioms for Church's system are as follows: 1. $p(qp)$, 2. $(s(pq))((sp)(sq))$, 3. $((pf)f)p$.

(v) A set of rules of inference which enable the deduction of theorems from other theorems or from axioms. There are two rules of inferences in Church's system, and these are essentially the same as in that of Whitehead and Russell; that is, (a) substitution, (b) *modus ponens*, which here can be put in the form: "From A and AB, infer B".

These five constituents complete the specification of the system, but it is convenient to make some definitions which simplify the writing out of results. Firstly, as well as the constant false proposition, it is convenient to have a constant true one, and we can define this in terms of f by the definition t=ff. It is also convenient from time to time to use the negation symbol of Whitehead and Russell, and this again can be defined by the following expression: $\sim A = Af$. Thirdly it is convenient to introduce the alternation operation of Whitehead and Russell by means of the expression: $A \lor B = (AB)B$. There is one more way in which we can simplify the expressions a little more. We notice that the axioms involve a rather large number of brackets. This is because two such expressions as $p(qr)$, $(pq)r$ have to be distinguished. But it is not necessary for this purpose to have brackets in *both* of these expressions. We could take pqr to represent one of them by convention and only insert brackets when we mean the other. It turns out to be most convenient to suppose bracketing to take place automatically on the left, so that pqr is to mean $(pq)r$, and when we wish to mean $p(qr)$ we must write it. The axioms can now be rewritten:

1. $p(qp)$
2. $s(pq)(sp(sq))$
3. $pffp$,

and the reader should verify that these expressions do unambiguously denote the same as the earlier ones. We shall now prove two or three theorems in Church's system, numbering these from 4 onwards, since we have three axioms.

Theorem 4 pp (that is, of course, $p \rightarrow p$, the "law of identity".)

Proof: $s \xrightarrow{(2)} q$: $q(pq)(qp(qq))$

    Modus ponens: $qp(qq)$

In this choose $p = (rq)$ & use Ax. 1.

Theorem 5 fp

Proof: $\left. \begin{array}{l} p \xrightarrow{(1)} pffp \\ q \longrightarrow f \end{array} \right\}$ f($pffp$) (after *modus ponens*)

$\left. \begin{array}{l} s \xrightarrow{(2)} f \\ p \longrightarrow pff \\ q \longrightarrow p \end{array} \right\}$ f(pff)(fp) (after *modus ponens*)

$\left. \begin{array}{l} p \xrightarrow{(1)} f \\ q \longrightarrow pf \end{array} \right\}$ f(pff)

Modus ponens gives the result.

Theorem 6 (pf)(pq)

Proof: $\left. \begin{array}{l} p \xrightarrow{(1)} fq \\ q \longrightarrow p \end{array} \right\}$ p(fq) (after *modus ponens*, using 5)

$$\left.\begin{array}{l} s \xrightarrow{(2)} p \\ p \longrightarrow f \end{array}\right\} \text{result, by } modus\ ponens.$$

(Note that, with our convention, this could be written $pf(pq)$ but the form given emphasises the structure more.)

We will now prove a general result about Church's system known as the deduction theorem. It is worthwhile here to draw a distinction between results of this kind which are theorems *about* the system, and the ones proved at the end of the last section which are theorems *in* the system. The theorems about the system are, naturally, proved in an informal manner (unless we decide that we need to formalise these as well, in which case we have to construct *another* system which "talks about" the first one).

In order to state the deduction theorem we need first to say precisely what we mean by *proof* in the system. Suppose that we have a sequence of well-formed formulae $B_1, B_2, \ldots B_m$. This sequence is said to form a proof of its last term (B_m) from a set of hypotheses $A_1, A_2, \ldots A_n$ if, at every stage of the sequence, that is, for every value of the suffix r, either:

(*a*) B_r is one of the hypotheses, or

(*b*) B_r comes by *modus ponens* from an earlier proposition, and so in fact from $B_j B_r$ where j is less than r, or

(*c*) B_r comes by substitution in an earlier B where, in particular the variable substituted for is not in any of the hypotheses.

(The reason for the proviso in (*c*) will be seen as the proof proceeds.) The reader should compare this definition of proof with any formal proof which he knows, taking note of the limited number of rules of inference allowed here. The subject in which proof is usually set out formally is, of course, geometry, and this definition of a proof is modelled on the way in which the geometrical proof is actually set out, although in geometry many other methods of inference are employed as well.

When we have a proof of the form described, we shall write $A_1, A_2, A_3 \ldots A_n \vdash B_m$. This sentence is to mean that there is a proof which begins with the given hypothesis and ends with B_m. Although this statement has a formal appearance, like a statement in the system, it is not a statement in the system, and is simply a convenient abbreviation of a statement *about* the system which could equally well be made in ordinary English.

We can now state the deduction theorem.

If $\qquad\qquad A_1, A_2, \ldots A_n \vdash B_m,$

then $\qquad\qquad A_1, A_2, \ldots A_{n-1}A_n \vdash B_m.$

Before proving this result we may notice how it connects the primitive connective of Church which we want to interpret as implication, with the provability which certainly is what we expect to mean by implication. In a sense the deduction theorem makes the statement about the system: "Implication means what you thought it would mean". Our proof of the deduction theorem simply takes the form of constructing the proof whose existence is stated in the conclusion of the theorem. We suppose in conformity with the assumptions of the theorem that the proof of B_m is $B_1, B_2 \ldots B_m$. We have now to show how to construct a proof of a new statement A_nB_m, and with this in mind we begin by writing down the following sequence of statements: $A_nB_1, A_nB_2, \ldots, A_nB_m$. Of course, unless we are extraordinarily lucky, this sequence of statements will not be a proof as we have defined proof above, because successive statements will not be related in the right way. What we can show, however, is that we can insert additional well-formed formulae into this sequence in such a way that not only is the finished product a proof of the last term, but *at every stage* the sequence including the new formulae up to that point is a proof of *its* last term. Let us see how this can be done. We suppose that it has been done up to a certain point in the sequence, say, B_i. A number of different cases arise, and we have to deal with them each according to its merits:

(a) It may happen that B_i is one of the assumptions, and this can arise in two ways. Let us first deal with the case when it is the assumption which is to be transferred to the other side of the proof sign; that is, A_n. In this case we observe that A_nB_i is A_nA_n, and this can be inferred from theorem 4. (To say that we can infer this from theorem 4 is really an abbreviated way of saying that in order to construct the sequence constituting a proof, we have to insert all the steps of the proof of theorem 4 together with a substitution stage in which the variable in theorem 4, which was p, is replaced by A_n. We shall use this abbreviated way of putting things in what follows.)

(b) In the case when B_i is one of the other assumptions, say $B_i = A_r (r \neq n)$, we use axiom 1 in the form $A_r(A_nA_r)$; that is $A_r(A_nB_i)$, and then deduce the required result by *modus ponens*.

(c) If B_i was derived by *modus ponens* in a scheme like the following

$$B_k$$
$$B_j = B_k B_i$$
$$\overline{}\ B_i$$

we shall have in our new sequence the propositions

$$A_n B_k$$
$$A_n(B_k B_i).$$

However, from axiom 2 we also have $A_n(B_k B_i)(A_n B_k(A_n B_i))$, and since the two previously mentioned propositions occur earlier in the sequence, and so by assumption have been proved, we can use *modus ponens* twice to deduce the result we require.

(*d*) Lastly it may happen that B_i comes by substitution in some earlier statement in the sequence, say, B_j. If this is so, then the same substitution serves also to turn $A_n B_j$ into $A_n B_i$, since the variable substituted for does not occur in any of the assumptions. We have therefore established that if the sequence can be filled in up to a particular stage it can always be filled in one stage further, and this proves the deduction theorem.

A simple corollary follows from this theorem. *If $A \vdash B$, then $\vdash AB$.* In this corollary we have used the proof sign without any of the hypotheses listed on the left of it. This means that the result stated follows directly from the axiom without any additional assumptions.

The deduction theorem can be used to give shorter proofs of the theorems already proved lengthily, and of new ones. We notice that the proof of the deduction theorem itself depended only on axioms 1 and 2, and theorem 4. It is therefore not illogical to use it to prove theorems 5 and 6, and we shall also use it to deduce three more theorems.

5. Ax 1. $\vdash f(pff)$

$\quad f \vdash pff$

By Ax 3: $f \vdash p$

Deduction Th: $\vdash fp$

6. $pf, p \vdash f$

But $\vdash fq$

Thus $pf, p \vdash q$

i.e. $\quad pf \vdash pq$

and so $\vdash pf(pq)$

   7. $p(qf)(pqf)$

   Proof: p, qf, $pq \vdash f$

so p, $qf \vdash pqf$

i.e. $p \vdash qf(pqf)$

and $\vdash p(qf)(pqf)$

   8. $pq(qr)(pr)$

   Proof: pq, $qr \vdash pr$

so $pq \vdash (qr)(pr)$

and $\vdash pq(qr)(pr)$

   9. $(pfr)(prr)$

   Proof: pr, rf, $\vdash pf$

   Thus pfr, pr, $rf \vdash r$

   Using this r in the rf, it follows that

               pfr, pr, $rf \vdash f$

i.e. pfr, $pr \vdash r\,ff$

   But $rffr$

The rest is easy.

In order to prove the decision theorem for Church's system (that is, the statement that every tautology is a theorem) we shall first prove a slightly different result from which the decision theorem easily follows. Suppose B to be any proposition in the system, and let $a_1, a_2 \ldots a_n$ be a set of variables which include all the variables occurring in B—and possibly others. We now consider a particular truth-valuation of these variables; that is, we assign to them, in any fashion, the values 1 and 0. Having done this we construct a new set of variables which somewhat resemble the old ones, but differ in the fact that they are all true, with the particular valuation given. In fact we define the new variables A_i by the rules

$$A_i = a_i \text{ if } |a_i| = 1, \ A_i = a_i f \text{ if } |a_i| = 0.$$

We then treat B in the same way by defining

$$B' = B \text{ if } |B| = 1, \ B' = Bf \text{ if } |B| = 0$$

When we have fixed up the variables and the proposition B in this way, our theorem is that $A_1, A_2, \ldots, A_n \vdash B'$.

The proof of this theorem is by induction, and it is in carrying out this proof that we need the simplifying property of Church's system, that it has only one connective. We carry out the induction over the number of occurrences of the connective in the proposition B. In order to start the proof, let us first consider the case where there are no connectives in B. In that case B is either f or it is one of the variables; say a_r. In the first case B' will therefore be ff and so we can prove B', since it is a special case of theorem 4. In the other case, B' is A_r, and therefore can be proved from the assumptions.

This starts the induction, and now we suppose that we have proved the theorem for all propositions which have less than n occurrences of the connective, and we shall then show that it is true for propositions with exactly n occurrences. Any such proposition B must fall apart into two principal sections B_1, B_2 joined by a connective. Accordingly we can be sure that from the "capital letter assumptions" we can prove both B_1' and B_2'. Several cases arise which have to be dealt with separately.

Firstly suppose that, with the particular valuation employed, B_2 is true. Accordingly $B_2' = B_2$, so that $B_1 B_2$ has the value 1, and therefore $B' = B$. Now from axiom 1 we have in particular $B_2(B_1 B_2)$, which can be written $B_2 B$. Since, however, we have a proof of B_2, we have a proof of B.

Secondly suppose that B_1 is false, so that $B_1' = B_1 f$. It again follows that $B_1 B_2$ is true, so that $B' = B$. Now a special case of theorem 6 is, as the reader may verify, $(B_1 f)(B_1 B_2)$. However, from the assumptions we have a proof of the left-hand part of this statement and so, by *modus ponens*, of the right-hand part, which is B.

The third case to consider is that when B_1 is true and B_2 is false. In that case B is false and so $B' = B_1 B_2 f$. Now a special instance of theorem 7 is $(B_1(B_2 f))(B_1 B_2 f)$, and from our induction assumption we have proofs both of B_1 and $B_2 f$. Accordingly we have a proof of the left-hand term, and we can therefore use *modus ponens* to detach it, giving us the right-hand term, which is B'. All cases are now covered, and so the induction can proceed.

We can now prove from this last result the *decision theorem* for Church's system. In the decision theorem we are concerned with tautologies; that is, we have a proposition B whose value is always 1 no matter what different valuations are given to the variables. The previous theorem related to one particular valuation. Now we have to apply it to each valuation in turn, but with the additional piece of information that, whatever valuation we choose, B' is always B. In other words, we have *both* of the following statements true about the propositions

$$A_1, A_2, \ldots, a_n \vdash B$$
$$A_1, A_2, \ldots, a_n f \vdash B.$$

As a result it follows that we have both

$$A_1, A_2, \ldots, A_{n-1} \vdash a_n B$$
$$A_1, A_2, \ldots, A_{n-1} \vdash a_n f B$$

However, a particular form of theorem 9 is, as the reader should verify, $(a_n f B)(a_n B B)$. The first part of this expression follows from the first $n-1$ assumptions, and so can be detached, and the first two terms of the second part also follow; and therefore B follows from the first $n-1$ assumptions. Continuing in this way we can eliminate all the hypotheses one at a time, and so construct a proof for any tautology.

Examples

1. Prove that $qr(pq(pr))$ is a tautology and try to carry out the construction of its proof by the method above.

7 THE LOGIC REQUIRED IN MATHEMATICS

BEFORE WE go any further in our construction of mathematics it will be a good thing to take stock of the point we have reached in constructing logic. We have taken the view that the results proved at the end of the last chapter show that the systems developed there (Church's or Whitehead and Russell's) are trivial ones. This was not at all the view originally taken. Rather people thought of elementary logic as a quite difficult system and viewed the results which we proved in Chapter 6 as showing certain short cuts whose existence also established special properties of the system. Amongst these special properties are two particularly important ones, consistency and completeness. Let us deal with these in turn.

The general idea of consistency is that one can prove only the correct things, not the incorrect ones. Therefore this general idea is not a property of the system *in itself*, but only of a particular interpretation of the system, since what is "correct" and what is not depends on how we interpret the symbols. We would like, therefore, to define a new concept which is as much like this general idea of consistency as possible but which is at the same time a property of the system itself, independent of its interpretation. There are several ways of doing this which are all more or less equivalent for the system which we considered. If the system has a negation operation, we can express consistency in the form "We cannot prove both p and *not-p*". In Church's system we have no negation operation in quite this sense, but instead we can define consistency by using pf instead of *not-p*. This definition of consistency agrees with our everyday concept since, in a consistent system, we can never reach a contradiction. So long, therefore, as *some* of the things which we can prove are things which we should normally interpret as true, our definition of consistency will agree entirely with the intuitive one. Moreover we have proved in the last chapter that Church's system is consistent, since the only results which can be proved are tautologies and only one out of p and *not-p* can possibly be a tautology.

Another definition of consistency which can be given is known as absolute consistency. This arises because, at least in the systems considered in the last two chapters, if we are allowed to assume any single result which does not follow from the axioms, we can prove *every* statement in the system, whether or not it is true. Thus, in such systems, any inconsistency at all shows up immediately in the very severe form that every statement can be proved; that is to say, the whole game of proof loses its value. Accordingly we define absolute consistency to mean that some statements are not theorems. It is clear that Church's system is also absolutely consistent since, for one thing, the constantly false proposition is a statement which cannot possibly be a tautology and therefore cannot be proved.

We pass now to the other important concept, that of completeness. The general idea of consistency was that one could only prove the "true" theorems. Similarly the idea of completeness is that one can prove *all* the "true" theorems. Here again we can reformulate this concept in terms of the system alone, irrespective of any particular interpretation. If there is a negation operation we can call the system complete if, for any statement, either we can prove the statement, or else the result of adjoining the statement to the axioms, as a new axiom, is to give a new system which is inconsistent (in the first sense of inconsistency). Similarly we can give a definition of completeness where the inconsistency in the second part of the definition is absolute and we can then call the system absolutely complete.

We can easily prove that Church's system is complete in the first sense. For suppose that A is not provable in the system; we know from the last chapter that this could only be the case if A is not a tautology. There exists, therefore, an assigning of truth values to the variables in A which gives the value zero to A. Let us construct a new statement, E say, by taking A and replacing each of the true variables in this assigning by t (where t is the universally true proposition defined in the last chapter) and replacing each of the false variables by the constant f. This new proposition certainly again has the value zero and so its negative, in Church's system Ef, is a tautology and can therefore (by the last chapter) be proved. If we now add E as an axiom, which is adding a special instance of A, it follows by the deduction theorem that we can prove f, and therefore prove every proposition, so that the system is evidently both inconsistent in the first sense and absolutely inconsistent. We have thus proved that Church's system is complete in both senses.

When the elementary logic of the last two chapters was first formulated it had a profound effect on people's opinions about mathematics and logic. Because of the evident triviality many people concluded that the same was true of mathematics as a whole. However, this is far from being the case. The logic of the last two chapters is completely inadequate for formulating anything but the most elementary mathematics. Ordinary mathematical statements usually take the form that all members of a certain class have a certain property. For example, "in any right angled triangle, the square on the hypoteneuse is the sum of the squares on the other two sides". It is of no interest to make this statement about one particular triangle; it becomes important because it applies to all right-angled triangles. Sometimes we make statements which do not apply to all numbers of a certain class but which assert the existence of some members of the class with a particular property. For example we might want to formulate the result of denying Fermat's last theorem in the form "There exists an integer n, greater than 2, such that there exist integers x, y, z with the property that

$$x^n + y^n = z^n".$$

(That we want to formulate such a statement is not, of course, any indication that we believe it to be true!)

Each of these kinds of statement, which are certainly necessary for mathematics, are more complicated than those which can be made by means of the logical systems of the last two chapters. We need to have what are called *quantified propositions*, something of the form

$$(x)[F(x)]$$

where the expression in square brackets is not actually a proposition until the variable x entering in it has been given a certain value and where the occurrence of x outside the square brackets denotes the phrase "for all x". As an example of such a statement we have

$$(x)[x + 1 = 1 + x]$$

where x may be thought of as a number, say as a positive integer. Similarly we shall need to consider statements of the form

$$(x)(y)[F(x, y)]$$

involving more than one variable, an example of this being

$$(x)(y)[x + y = y + x].$$

Expressions like $F(x)$, $F(x, y)$ play much the same role in logic as *functions* do in ordinary mathematics. Thus sin x does not denote a number, but sin is an operator, with the property that sin x becomes a number whenever x is given a numerical value, as for example, sin $\pi/6 = \frac{1}{2}$. For this reason, $F(x)$ is called a *propositional function*; $x + 1 = 1 + x$ is not a proposition, but $1 + 2 = 2 + 1$ is. The question of the other kind of quantified proposition in which the existence of a number is asserted, is closely connected with this kind, since we can define the second kind by an expression like

$$(\exists x)[F(x)] \equiv \sim\{(x)[\sim F(x)]\}$$

The reader may immediately verify that this agrees with his everyday intuition in the obvious interpretation.

Whitehead and Russell carried out this generalisation of logic and it is fairly clear, intuitively, although this is a question which really requires a long and subtle proof starting from a precise definition, that such an augmented system is adequate for describing elementary arithmetic. We shall see in later chapters that no decision procedure can possibly exist for such a system. Before we do this, however, let us see what use Whitehead and Russell make of this system.

One of the problems which Whitehead and Russell were most concerned with was, as we have seen, to construct the foundations of elementary arithmetic, as a first step between the foundations of all mathematics. The basic mathematical concepts in elementary arithmetic are the whole numbers, so that the first problem is to construct these. Evidently the first and major step here is to construct the integer 1, since when we have once started, with the first number, it will be easy to augment the definition so that we can go on to the higher ones. The following definition of the number 1 is not completely identical to that of Whitehead and Russell, but is much the same as theirs and is slightly simplified for our purposes:

$$1 = \hat{x}(x \neq \phi \ \& \ (y \varepsilon x.\&.z \varepsilon x] \rightarrow y = z).$$

(Here ϕ denotes the empty set.) Let us try to see exactly what Whitehead and Russell meant by this formula. In the first place we notice that the number is defined by means of the notation introduced in Chapter 4 as a *set* of objects x. We may remark here that this, apparently rather high-brow, definition agrees very well with the way in which we are actually introduced to numbers in everyday life. If we wish to explain the number 3 to a child we go through a process which is essentially that of indicating a large number of diverse collections of three things, apples, chairs and so on, until eventually the child makes the required abstraction and realises what property it is that all these triads have in common.

We come now to consider the properties which are used in the above definition to define the x's, the set of which is to represent the number 1. The first bracket of the definition merely assures us that x is not the null set, with no members. The second part then tells us something about the individuals which belong to x. From both of these parts it is clear then that x itself must be a set, so that the number is being defined as a set of sets. Let us look more closely at the second part of the definition. This states that, if we have any two members of x, these two must in fact be the same, i.e. that x cannot have two different members. The sets x, then, all have only a single member, and so we see that the definition of Whitehead and Russell for the number 1 is simply that it is the set of all unit sets, meaning, by a unit set, a set with only one member. When put into words this definition seems circular but it is not so in fact. To have written such a definition was a very great achievement in human thought since people had for many years regarded the whole numbers as something which could not be further analysed.

However, the definition is not without difficulty. It is couched in terms of a set theory but clearly this set theory cannot be the simple one of Cantor, since, as we have seen this contains paradoxes and is therefore evidently inconsistent. In particular, Cantor's set theory contains Russell's paradox which can be written in the form

$$R = \hat{x}[\sim(x\varepsilon x)]$$

(This is the expression which defines a set which gives rise to a contradiction whether we suppose that it belongs to itself or not.) Clearly we have to dodge Russell's paradox somehow. The method adopted by Whitehead and Russell for this purpose is known as the *theory of types*. They decided that the cause of trouble in Russell's paradox was in allowing anything to belong to itself. They proposed accordingly to divide everything up into types. Objects of type 0 were called individuals. Sets of individuals were said to be of type 1. Sets of objects of type 1 were said to be of type 2, and so on. The expression

$$x\varepsilon y$$

was only to be allowed as a sensible expression if y was of type exactly one higher than x. Of course in such a system Russell's paradox is avoided though whether other paradoxes may arise is not so clear.

When we go back to our definition of the number 1, however, we are in grave difficulty. In this definition y and z must evidently be of the same type, x is therefore of type one higher and the number is defined as a set of x's and is therefore of type one higher again. According to our choice for the y's and z's we could define numbers of types 2, 3, 4, etc., but this was not what we intended at all. What sort of arithmetic would it be if we want to add the 1 of type 2 to that of type 3? We wanted to have a single number 1 defined.

Whitehead and Russell decided to cut their way out of this tangle by what they call the axiom of reducibility. We do not want to go too far into the technical details of their system here but roughly speaking this axiom says that if we can define a mathematical object of a certain type there will exist corresponding objects of every other type. Although we are not entering into the technical details, it is important to get the general feel of this result. We started with Cantor's admittedly inconsistent set theory. By means of the theory of types Russell's paradox is removed and possibly all other paradoxes as well. Let us at any rate taken an optimistic view here, and suppose that the theory of types removes all the paradoxes. We then introduced an axiom of the general spirit that although types are important sometimes, we can ignore them most of the time. It is obvious that such an assumption unbars the door to the possibility of inconsistency entering again. The attempt to base mathematics on an unshakable logical foundation is not viable. The theory of types itself was not an acknowledged piece of logic but one could perhaps imagine that it was implicit in classical logic; but the axiom of reducibility is neither a logical axiom nor something which gives rise to an obviously consistent system. The need for this axiom was the major factor in the disillusionment of mathematicians with the Whitehead-Russell system.

Examples

1. (Aristotle's *Principle of the Absolute*.) Consider the formula:

$$(\exists a)(\exists b)Fab. \rightarrow .(\exists c)(x)[x \neq c \rightarrow (Fxc \& \sim Fcx)]$$

where Fab is a relation (read as "a has the relation F to b").

(i) Interpret the formula in words.

(ii) Let Fab mean "a is moved by b"; the interpretation of the formula is then that c is Aristotle's "prime mover".

(iii) Let Fab mean "a is desired for the sake of b". The interpretation is then that c is Aristotle's *summum bonum*.

(iv) Give an instance of the truth and the falsehood of Aristotle's principle amongst the positive integers. (Hints: a, b positive integers, Fab means $a > b$, and c is then zero; a, b positive integers, Fab means $b > a$, and the principle is false. Accordingly, as Kant pointed out, the principle cannot be a reliable instrument of proof.)

8 HILBERT'S METAMATHEMATICS

THE VIEW of mathematics held by the Hilbert school which will be described in this chapter originated before the failure of "Principia Mathematica" became clear. Nonetheless it is probably correct to see it as very much stimulated and helped forward by the evident hopelessness of basing mathematics on logic. The view of Hilbert was that, in attempting to base mathematics on logic, one was attempting a very much too ambitious project. The fundamental ideas of logic rested on the difficult concepts of truth and falsehood. Such concepts had given rise to trouble for philosophers over a long period, and it was not to be expected that these troubles could be cleared out of the way overnight and the difficulties of mathematics solved at the same time. Hilbert approached the problem in what we now see to be a truly scientific manner, by proposing to cut it up into a number of small problems which could be tackled separately. He proposed to leave on one side all questions of truth, and to concentrate instead on mathematics as a formal system. Amongst some of his later followers this view seems to have been distorted into the view that considerations of truth had no place in the foundations of mathematics. Hilbert himself did not take such an extreme view. Rather he took the view—with an encouraging humility—that the difficult questions could perhaps, if we are lucky, be set on one side until after the paradoxes have been disposed of. This approach may be related to the fact that he had no predisposition towards working in the foundations of mathematics, being by nature a mathematician whose delight was in the solution of difficult problems. He found, however, that he was unable to justify the methods which he wished to use without strengthening the foundations of the subject. He was driven again and again to return to these questions of foundations in order to be sure that the system in which he was working was really safe.

We shall only have a really clear understanding of the situation in mathematics (and in logic) now if we connect it with its historical preliminaries. In fact we must go as far back as Aristotle. Aristotle looked on a *deductive science* as a set, S, of sentences such that

(i) each sentence in S refers to a set of real objects,

(ii) each sentence in S is true,

(iii) S contains the logical consequences of any two members of S,

(iv) S contains some undefined terms, whose meaning is obvious, and in terms of which any other terms in S can be defined,

(v) S contains some unproved sentences, whose truth is obvious, and from which all the other sentences of S can be proved.

Such an ideal theory could not, of course, outlast the growth of experimental science in the seventeenth century. Accordingly men began to distinguish rational science (e.g. mathematics), in which (i) was no longer required, from empirical science, in which (iii) (iv) (v) were not always demanded (because experiment would take their place). But the paradoxes of set theory already begin to show that (iv) is not universally tenable; and the most serious consequence of later investigations is the result of Gödel (Chapter 9) that even (v) cannot be maintained.

If we agree to set on one side considerations of truth, then the *axioms* of a mathematical system become simply a set of statements which we distinguish at the beginning as being in a certain class, the other members of this class being the *theorems* which may be derived from the axioms by given rules of inference. So long as we keep out of sight all questions of the truth of the axioms and theorems, the whole procedure can be likened to a game played with symbols on a piece of paper, and this picture of it is the one conjured up by the name "formalist" given to those of Hilbert's school. Of course there is a little more to be said. We want to be sure that the game is an interesting one, that it is being played according to a reasonable set of rules, and that it agrees—at least roughly—with the "games" given the same name in ordinary developments of mathematics (that is, if we are given a set of axioms for geometry (which was actually one of the first problems tackled by Hilbert) we want to be sure that the set of theorems generated by these axioms really correspond more or less to the theorems in geometry as usually understood). To be a little more precise, we want to be sure that the axiom system allows us actually to prove only some of the possible statements in the system, and not others, so that it *is* a worthwhile game investigating whether any particular statements follow from the axioms or not. In terms of the wording of the last chapter, we want the axiom system to be consistent. Similarly we want to be sure of being able to prove, in our refurbished mathematics, as much as could be proved before we start; that is, the axiom system ought to be complete. As an aesthetic matter it was also considered desirable that the axioms should be independent; that is, that no one of them could be derived as a theorem in the system defined by the remaining ones. If we use an axiom system which is not independent, we do not run into any great trouble. We are simply assuming a little more than is necessary. It is not, therefore, anything like so important to establish the independence of the axioms as it is to establish their consistency and completeness, and we shall here disregard all questions of independence.

By what means are we to establish consistency and completeness? In the previous chapter we did this for a particular system by means of arguments which were not *in* the system, but were phrased in normal English in terms of results *about* the system. The same situation will hold in any mathematical system. Insofar as the arguments about the system have to be derived from certain assumptions by the usual logical forms and arguments, they can be said to constitute another subject, metamathematics, which deals with mathematical systems in just the same way as mathematics deals with numbers, geometrical figures, and so on. It might be necessary in particularly subtle metamathematical arguments to formalise the metamathematics as well; and in that case the formal system for the metamathematics will need to be discussed by yet another system outside it. Generally speaking, however, the metamathematical system will have a very much simpler logical structure than the original system, so that it is rarely necessary to proceed to a second step. If we do go on to a second step, we shall expect to be working in a very simple logical system indeed, and a third step will never be necessary.

It will serve to illustrate what we mean by a metamathematical question if we consider a very simple formal system S with the following structure:

4

1. Alphabet of $S = \{x\}$.

2. One operator, a binary one, $|$, so that the well-formed formulae are defined by:
   (a) x is a *wff*.
   (b) If A, B are *wffs*, so is $|AB$.

3. There is one rule of inference:
   From any *wff* P, we can infer $|Px$.

4. One axiom: $|xx$.

With such a formal system we can ask, for instance, whether the formula x is provable (it clearly is not).

We can now formulate in a little more detail the programme of the Hilbert school. It was, firstly, to formulate the appropriate formal system for each individual branch of mathematics. Secondly, it was to construct a metamathematics which would establish the completeness and consistency of each of these systems. The work on geometry started at the end of the 19th century, and from then until 1930 considerable progress was made with this programme. One after another formal systems were constructed, and the consistency of these systems was shown to depend on the consistency of elementary arithmetic. It is a little difficult to give the details here for these systems, and we shall content ourselves with an analogy from another branch of mathematics in which such a consistency proof was given earlier in the 19th century.

The example which we are going to describe in detail arises in geometry. It is well-known that geometers from Euclid onwards—and possibly earlier—were worried by the rather different nature of the so-called "parallel postulate" compared with the other assumptions of geometry. This is the postulate which states (to give one form) that if a line l cuts two other lines in such a way that the sum of the interior angles between these lines and l is less than two right-angles, these lines will interesect on the side of l for which this is the case. Many attempts were made to show that Euclid's axiom system was not independent, and that the parallel postulate could be derived from the others. But these attempts failed. In some cases the attempt was made in the following form: it was assumed that the parallel postulate was false, and it was therefore replaced by some other statement which was clearly inconsistent with it. The results of adding this statement to the remaining axioms of Euclidean geometry were investigated in the hopes that a contradiction would result. Such a contradiction would have shown the inconsistency of denying the parallel postulate and accepting the other axioms, and so would have shown that the parallel postulate followed from the other axioms. These particular attempts were the most valuable ones because, although they did not succeed in proving the parallel postulate, they did succeed in constructing alternative geometries

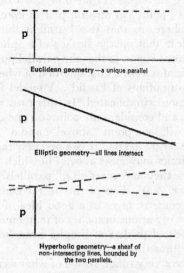

Euclidean geometry—a unique parallel

Elliptic geometry—all lines intersect

Hyperbolic geometry—a sheaf of
non-intersecting lines, bounded by
the two parallels.

Figure 8.

to Euclid's. One such geometry is that in which, from a point outside a line, no parallel can be drawn to the line; all lines intersect somewhere. Another geometry is that in which, from a point outside a line, a whole sheaf of lines can be drawn which do not intersect it; the two bounding lines of the sheaf qualifying for the title of parallels. These two cases are known as the elliptic and hyperbolic geometries (*Figure 8*).

The problem for the people who wanted a proof of the parallel postulate was to show that the elliptic and hyperbolic geometries were inconsistent. They failed in this because these geometries are not inconsistent, at least if Euclidean geometry itself is consistent.

The way in which we can see this is to construct within the framework of Euclidean geometry a set of mathematical objects satisfying all the axioms of the elliptic and hyperbolic geometries. If an inconsistency could result in these systems, it would therefore involve an inconsistency in Euclidean geometry as well. The elliptic case is an easy model to construct. We simply notice that all the axioms given by Euclid—except the parallel postulate—are automatically satisfied on the surface of a sphere where "straight line" is interpreted to mean great circle (*Figure 9 (a)*). To be more precise we have to interpret "point" to mean a pair of diametrically opposite points on the sphere, so that two "straight lines" meet any one "point". It is clear that on the surface of a sphere any two great circles intersect somewhere, so that the parallel postulate is certainly not true (and this also answers the question of whether it is independent of other assumptions of Euclid). A model for the hyperbolic case is a little more complicated. In this case we draw a line *l*, say, in the plane, and consider only points on one side of *l*. A "point" in the geometry will be a point "above" *l* and a "straight line" will be a circle whose centre lies on *l* (more precisely the part of the circle above *l*). Two circles may meet above *l* in which case they do so at only one point, or they may meet on *l*, "parallels", or they may not meet at all (*Figure 9 (b)*). This picture of the consistency proofs for non-Euclidean geometry gives us a good idea of how the problem of the consistency of various branches of mathematics were reduced by the Hilbert school to that of simpler branches, and eventually to elementary arithmetic.

Let us now give a very rough sketch of what went wrong with the Hilbert programme in 1930, so that we can fill out the details of this sketch in the next chapter. The problem is now the consistency and completeness of elementary arithmetic. We are here dealing with a fairly simple formal system. It will involve some of the logical symbols of the last chapter, with possibly one or two more in addition, some arithmetical symbols like o and 1, $+$ **and** $=$, and one or two more mathematical symbols of this kind. It is clear that any formula in this formal system, consisting as it does of a row of symbols, drawn from a comparatively small alphabet, can be related to a set of numbers which can be calculated simply by numbering off the elements of the alphabet and writing them down instead of the original symbols. There is nothing more complicated at issue here than a matter of coding. An ordinary English sentence can be coded as a sequence of integers by defining $A=1$, $B=2$, . . . , $Z=26$,

Stop=27, with perhaps the further refinement of Capital letter=28, space=29. Not that this code is of any great value, but it does achieve the object of making it a purely arithmetical question whether a certain English sentence is constructed according to fixed rules of grammar or not. Similarly in our system the question of whether or not a sequence of formulae is a proof of the formula which concludes the sequence is a question of whether a sequence of sets of integers satisfies certain conditions. If we put these conditions into an arithmetical form, we can see that the question of whether

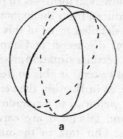

a

Model of elliptic geometry—great circles
on a sphere

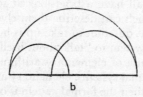

b

Model of hyperbolic geometry
Figure 9.

a sequence is a proof or not can be reformulated as a statement in elementary arithmetic, and therefore can be stated *within the system itself*. It is then possible, inside the system, to make statements about whether certain formulae in the system can be proved. It may even be possible to formulate inside the system a statement like the following (which here of course we must formulate in ordinary English, since we have not elaborated the system precisely yet):

This sentence in a box on this page is unprovable .

The reader may contrast this perfectly reasonable sentence with the paradoxical one in Chapter 1. If we can formulate such a sentence inside the system, we can then ask whether or not the sentence is provable. If the sentence were to be provable, then we should be able to prove that it was not provable, which is evidently an inconsistency, so that in this case elementary arithmetic is inconsistent. On the other hand, if the sentence were not to be provable, it is clearly a true sentence, so that in any reasonable definition of completeness elementary arithmetic is incomplete in the sense that the sentence—in its arithmetical form—is an evidently true sentence which yet cannot be deduced from the axioms. In the next chapter we shall investigate the detailed proof of this situation more fully.

Both from the general discussion in Chapter 1 and that in the last section we see that a peculiar situation arises as soon as a language (in the sense of a formal system) is able to describe itself. If there is present in the language, as in English, the very subtle ideas of truth and falsehood this may well lead to a paradox, that is, to nonsense. If the ideas of truth and falsehood are carefully exluded, it still leads to incompleteness. Our task in the next chapter will be to sketch out the details of this leading to incompleteness, since we have only described it here in a very imprecise manner. Before we do this, however, we shall have a brief look at some general features of formal systems which can describe themselves.

The first important question to take up is how it is possible for a fairly simple formal system to "talk about itself". We shall find that the key here is the use of elementary arithmetic. This is because, for a large class of formal systems, elementary arithmetic is adequate to describe them. If then the formal system is one which can in turn describe elementary arithmetic the system will be able to talk about itself. A system describing elementary arithmetic will be one which talks about itself. Now a system describing elementary arithmetic will be one which talks about properties of the integers; let us see, then, what sort of things we need to describe such properties.

We need to have logic, in the way in which we developed it, including the quantifiers so that we can make statements about "all numbers". For this purpose we need at least one logical operator, for which the Sheffer stroke will suffice, some logical variables (like p and q in the previous chapters) and a quantifier symbol. We can economise in the number of variables that we need by exactly the same trick as a mathematician employs when he uses for his variables x, x', x'' . . . . . For convenience in the later working, it will be better for us not to employ a dash, i.e. not to write p, p', p'', . . . for variables, but to define an operator d so that if p is any variable dp is another variable, ddp is another and so on. In this way we can have as many variables as we wish for the expenditure of only two letters of the (English) alphabet. We shall use the Polish notation for the Sheffer stroke so as to avoid the use of brackets and to conform with the notation for the rest of the system we may as well use a letter, say S, for it, instead of the stroke in the previous notation. Of course, this economical notation will not usually be a very convenient one for actual working, either in arithmetic or logic. Even such a simple statement as the axiom

$$p \vee q \rightarrow q \vee p$$

has to be re-written, by noting that

$$Spq = \sim(p \ \& \ q),$$

so that

$$S: \sim p . \sim q = p \vee q,$$

and

$$S: p . \sim q = \sim p \vee q = p \rightarrow q,$$

in the form

$$S(p \vee q) . \sim (q \vee p),$$

i.e. as

$$SSSppSqqSSSppSqqSSSppSqq.$$

(The reader should verify that the new form can be *unambiguously* dissected into the old one.)

We have thus constructed a logical formalism, and we now want to use it to make statements in elementary arithmetic. In these statements we need of course, both numerical variables and also actual numbers. As far as the numerical variables are concerned we can economise again and choose a particular one, which we denote by n, and we can then make as many more as we wish with the help of our d operator. In the case of actual numbers we can also economise but it is desirable not to use the same operator d but rather to have a *successor relation s* which applied to any number gives the next higher one. (The reason for this distiction is as follows: numerical variables like n, dn, ddn, . . . are quantities for which numbers need to be substituted. If a is any number, and we consider the special case of some general result, involving the variable *n*, in which *n* is replaced by the number *a*, the notation *da* for another number would suggest that *dn*, if it occurred, should be replaced by *da*, whereas, of course, *dn* is simply another variable, which may be replaced by any other number. Another way of putting this distinction is to remark that *n*, *dn*, *ddn* . . . are *any* variables; we do not need a notation for *any numbers*, but for the positive integers in a particular order). All we need then, as well as *s*, is a starting point and this will be provided by the number zero. Now we need to have also some arithmetical operators, which we shall write entirely in the Polish notation. We need operators for addition and multiplication and we must also have the relation which states when numbers are equal.

Collecting all these requirements together we see that a very economical system which is none the less adequate for arithmetic is provided by the following list of symbols which are here set out somewhat like the characters in a Restoration comedy:

(*a*) 1. *p*, a variable

2. *d*, a dash (so, *dp* is *p'* a new variable)

3. *S*, a Sheffer stroke (in Polish notation, so *SAB* is a proposition when *A* and *B* are)

(*b*) 4. *A*, a quantifier (all, so *NAN* is another quantifier, where *N* is not, made from *S*)

(*c*) 5. *n*, a numerical variable (to which *d* can be applied)

6. *P*, an arithmetical plus

7. *T*, an arithmetical times } (all in Polish)

8. *E*, an arithmetical equals

(*d*) 9. *s*, a successor relation

0. o, a cypher

The particular cast given here for our comedy has the advantage of being only ten in number so that any statement which we can make with these symbols, which will therefore be a string of symbols, can be translated at once unambiguously into a string of numbers between o and 9 according to the numbers on the left-hand side of the list. This string of numbers can then be interpreted as the expression of some (usually large) integer in the scale of ten. For example, the statement "one and one is two" becomes in our notation *EPsososso* and this can be rewritten in numerical form as

869,090,990, a very large but none-the-less well-defined number. For more complicated sentences the numbers rapidly become very large. For example

$$(x)(y)(x+y=y+x)$$

becomes

$$AnAdnESndnSdnn,$$

or, in numerical form

$$45,425,835,253,255.$$

Every statement in the system is therefore represented by a positive integer.

Our system is clearly adequate for describing elementary arithmetic, that is, for describing properties of the integers. Once we realise this, however, we can see that something somewhere is not quite right. Let us consider how many properties of the integers we can talk about. Since each such property is to be a statement in the system and therefore will have a number, according to our method of numbering described in the last section, there cannot be more properties of the integers described than there are integers. It is true that this number is infinite. But we learnt in Chapter 4 that we can still draw distinctions between different infinite numbers. In particular the set of all real numbers between 0 and 1 was there shown to be more numerous (in a rather obvious sense) than the set of integers. Let us, then, look at matters from a different point of view. We can describe a property of the integers by stating which integers have a property and which have not. If we write down all the integers in ascending order of magnitude and write underneath each of them a 1 if the integer has the property in question, and a 0 otherwise, we derive a row of 0's and 1's. Any such row can, by the simple device of putting a decimal point at the beginning of it, be regarded as the decimal expansion (in the scale of two) of some number between 0 and 1. For example the property of being even has the scheme

$$0 \quad 1 \quad 2 \quad 3 \quad 4 \quad 5 \quad 6 \quad 7 \ldots$$
$$1 \quad 0 \quad 1 \quad 0 \quad 1 \quad 0 \quad 1 \quad 0 \ldots$$

with corresponding decimal form

$$. \ 1 \ 0 \ 1 \ 0 \ 1 \ 0 \ldots,$$

which is the expression, in the scale of two, of the number

$$\frac{1}{2}+\frac{1}{8}+\frac{1}{32}+ \ldots = \frac{\frac{1}{2}}{1-\frac{1}{4}}=\frac{2}{3}.$$

Similarly the property of being odd corresponds to the number $\frac{1}{3}(=1-\frac{2}{3}$, why?), whilst being prime (and greater than 1, to complete the definition unambiguously) is represented by the decimal

. o o 1 1 o 1 o 1 o o o 1...

There will, then, be as many properties of the integers as there are numbers between o and 1. If our formal system really fitted, this would lead us to think that there are only as many numbers between o and 1 as there are statements of properties of integers, i.e. as many as the integers themselves, so that we could number all the numbers between o and 1, giving each a positive integer as its number. But this was precisely what we showed to be impossible in Chapter 4, so that there cannot be enough statements in the system to describe all the properties. This argument is very direct, and shows that something is wrong somewhere, but it does not give us any clear indication of where the trouble lies. This we shall take up in the next chapter.

Examples

1. Consider the following axioms

A. $Rxy \rightarrow \sim Ryx$

B. $Rxy \ \& \ Ryz. \rightarrow. Rxz$

C. $(x)(\exists y). Ryx$

(i) Prove that one way of interpreting these is as representing positions of points on an (infinite) straight line, Rxy meaning "x is to the right of y".

(ii) Prove that C is independent of A & B by giving another interpretation of R (viz. let Rxy mean that "x divides y", x, y, z now being integers).

(iii) Notice that it is not necessary for this purpose that arithmetic should all be *true* (only that it should be consistent).

(iv) Prove that the axioms A, B, C are consistent (assuming arithmetic is) by interpreting Rxy as "y divides x".

(v) Prove that the axioms A, B, C are *incomplete*, since they cannot prove

$$(x)(\exists y).Rxy$$

[Hint: Prove the independence of this from A, B, C by means of the interpretations of (iv).]

9 GÖDEL'S PROOF

LET US now take up the problem of deciding just where the formal system which we have described above fails to fit elementary arithmetic. We shall suppose that the system is adequate for making all the statements about relations between the integers that we shall need in the argument. This assumption may well be questioned by the reader. To establish it is a task of no intrinsic difficulty, but needing a great deal of detailed and painstaking work, so that we omit it here. This is the only respect—admittedly a major one—in which our discussion falls short of completeness.

We have, then, our ten symbols, and any single statement in the system, being a row of these symbols, corresponds to a number, which is found by translating the symbols into numerical form and regarding the resultant row as a number in the scale of 10. Let us now go on to consider the idea of a *proof* in the formal system. A proof in this system, exactly as in the simpler system of Church for the propositional calculus, which we discussed in Chapter 6, will consist of a *sequence of statements* in the system which stand in a certain relation to each other. Accordingly a proof in the system can be translated into a sequence of numbers, each of which occurs in the process of describing the formal system by means of arithmetic, and these are called the *Gödel numbers* of the statements, of the form

$$g_1, g_2, \ldots, g_n.$$

Instead of using a *sequence* of Gödel numbers of statements, however, it is convenient to write instead what is called the *Gödel number of the proof*, in the form

$$2^{g_1} 3^{g_2} 5^{g_3} \ldots p_r{}^{g_r} \ldots p_n{}^{g_n}$$

where p_r is the rth prime.

It is well-known that an integer can be written as a product of prime factors in only one way (at least this is true if elementary arithmetic is consistent—an assumption which we shall certainly be making. If elementary arithmetic is inconsistent we are in an even worse situation than we thought). If we write down the Gödel number of a proof we can factorise it into its prime factors, write down the indices of the various primes which enter, translate back each of these numbers into statements in the system, and so reconstitute the whole proof. The Gödel number of a proof therefore tells us everything about it. Of course the Gödel numbers will be very large, and the actual carrying out of the programme which we have just described will be virtually impossible in anyone's lifetime for a number of any reasonable length. This fact is quite unimportant here; the important thing is the theoretical possibility of specifying the proof completely by a single number.

We can now rephrase the idea of a statement having a proof in arithmetical terms. Roughly speaking, we are going to say that a statement has a proof if and only if there is a number, which is the Gödel number of a proof of the statement. This apparently insignificant change is of the greatest importance, since it rephrases the idea of something being provable, in arithmetical terms. We must now be a little more precise about this. Let us confine ourselves to proofs of properties of the integers. (The reader may well like to think in the first part of this proof of some particular property such as being prime.) We will then have some one-place predicate representing the property, which will be able to be expressed entirely in our formalism but which, for shortness, we write as $F(x)$ where x is some numerical variable. (For example x could be the particular numerical variable listed in our previous chapter as n, but it might be another one derived from n by applying the dash operator.) What we have to do is to find some way of specifying the predicate in terms of the Gödel numbers. For this purpose we fix on one particular variable, and it is natural to choose n, since it is the simplest one. We then can specify the predicate uniquely by giving the Gödel number of $F(n)$, which we denote by $|F(n)|$, as μ. Next let ν be any integer (written out, of course, in terms of the notation of the last chapter). We can then define a certain function of these two integers, which we denote by $s(\mu, \nu)$ as follows: $s(\mu, \nu)$ is the Gödel number of the formula $F(\nu)$ when μ is defined as above, unless it should happen that μ is not actually the Gödel number of any expression like $F(n)$, in which case we define $s(\mu, \nu)$ as zero. Since the function $s(\mu, \nu)$ is simply an arithmetical function of two integers with integral values, it is a function in elementary arithmetic, and so can be constructed in the system we have defined. (Here we use the fact that the system is adequate for elementary arithmetic.)

We now have to construct a certain statement in our formal system. Taking any two numbers μ and ν we can ask the question whether one of these—μ—is the Gödel number of a proof of the statement whose Gödel number is ν. Whether this is so or not is a question of whether the indices of the primes in the decomposition of μ into prime factors stand in a certain relation to each other, and whether also the final index is ν. If this situation is the case we can say that a certain relation, $D(\mu, \nu)$, holds between μ and ν, and this relation is a purely arithmetical relation, and so should also be expressible in the formal system. Once we have constructed the function s and the relation D we are able to say something about provability. In fact a formula whose Gödel number is ν can be said to be *provable* when $(NAn)ND(n, \nu)$. (Here $(NAn)N$ is short-hand for the more complicated quantifier "there exists n" written out at length in our system.)

We have now constructed the general framework, and we want to go on and construct the particular statement which was expressed in words in paragraph 5 of the last chapter. With this in mind let us consider the following statement

$$S(n, p) = (NAm)ND(m, s(n, p))$$

where m and p are variables in the system definitely different from n. (For example we might have

$$m = dn, \quad p = ddn$$

but it is not necessary for the purpose of our argument to specify m and p exactly.) The expression S is now a statement involving two variables. Notice that it is not a proposition; it will only become a proposition when particular values are substituted for m and p. Our first step is to form a new predicate, that is, a property of a single variable, by taking m and p to be equal. We therefore have

$$S(n, n) = (NAm)ND(m, s(n, n))$$

as a convenient expression for this property of the integers, whatever it may be. Let us now direct our attention to the negative of this property which we can accordingly write as

$$NS(n, n) = N(NAm)ND(m, s(n, n)).$$

This negative is a certain property of the integers, and we can compute the Gödel number of the expression; so

$$|NS(n, n)| = g.$$

This computation will land us up with a number of colossal size it is true, but nonetheless perfectly definite. We can imagine ourselves substituting this particular integer for the variable n in the expression whose Gödel number is g. When we do this we reach, at last, a proposition. Whether or not this proposition is true is of course quite another matter, but at least we have here a proposition about a certain large integer which can be expressed inside the system. Let us ask ourselves what is the significance of this proposition $NS(g, g)$. It states that there is no proof of a certain formula in the system, and this formula is specified by means of the function S. In fact the formula which this proposition alleges (possibly slanderously) to be without proof, is a certain property of the integer g which we can abbreviate in the form $F(g)$ where F is itself defined by the condition that $|F(n)|=g$. Of course to give the Gödel number of F in this way is to specify it uniquely. We can, before sitting down to do any complicated calculations, cast about to see where we can spot a formula which has the right Gödel number because, if we can, we can be sure it will be F. Looking back, we see that F in this case is already provided by the formula

$$NS(n, n) = N(NAm) ND(m, s(n, n)).$$

But this formula has to be considered now with the variable n replaced by a particular number g, so that it has the form $NS(g, g)$. This was exactly the formula we were setting out to interpret, so that we see, finally, that this formula has the property of asserting that it cannot itself be proved. Exactly as in the last chapter we can consider whether the formula is true or not. If it were to be false, then it would be false to suppose that the formula could not be proved, so that it would be provable, and at the same time false, which makes elementary arithmetic inconsistent. Since this cannot be the case according to our assumptions, we have to take the other alternative that the formula is true and therefore unprovable. Since it is a formula in elementary arithmetic, we are forced to the conclusion that this particular formalisation of elementary arithmetic is incomplete in the sense that it cannot prove all the valid formulae. However, it is perfectly obvious that another formulation of elementary arithmetic could have an exactly similar proof carried through for it. The essential feature of the proof is that as soon as the work can talk about elementary arithmetic it is strong enough to talk about itself, and then the incompleteness arises.

We can now fill out details of what went wrong with the Hilbert programme in 1930. The search for a complete axiom system was doomed to failure. Actually the situation is a little worse, because Gödel was able to go on and prove that amongst the unprovable statements in the formalism was one whose obvious interpretation was that the formalism was consistent. The details of this are a little beyond the scope of the present book, but if we take it for granted for the moment we can see that not only was the search for a complete axiom system a hopeless one, but also that any axiom system could not have its consistency established within a formal system defined by it. In fact the consistency could only be proved in a "bigger" system whose consistency was therefore even more in doubt.

We therefore see that an inevitable consequence of our method of constructing a formal language, as soon as it reaches a high level of precision, is this curious property of undecidability. We could very well have started out with the idea of constructing a language of formal deduction whose consequence in terms of provable statements would have been exactly those accessible to our insight. In fact, however, insight and deduction give sets of consequences which are certainly overlapping, but neither contains the other. On the one hand deduction is so powerful that it can, as we are well aware, produce many complicated results which are beyond the power of insight. This is not so surprising as the situation on the other hand, thrown up in the present chapter, that deduction will always be unable to prove all the truths which are accessible to insight.

The principal lesson of a positive character which we can draw from the rather depressing result of Gödel (notwithstanding the tremendous human achievement which his proof constitutes) is that of the importance of arithmetic. Any careful investigation of just what can be proved in a formal system, and so any further attack on the difficulties thrown up by Gödel's theorem, could just as well be considered as an investigation in arithmetic. The fundamental question would then be: what numbers can we calculate? If a certain number which corresponds to the number of a proof can be calculated, then we have a demonstration of the existence of the proof, and therefore a demonstration of provability. What we have to do then, is to determine when a number, or, more generally, a set of numbers depending on the positive integers, can be calculated. Since these numbers depend on the positive integers, what we are confronted here with is a function of the integers, and we have to ask ourselves when this function, which we believe we have defined, is *really* defined, in the sense that its value can be calculated whenever we wish.

Let us first consider one or two simple examples of functions of the integers, which are certain to be useful in formulating any arithmetical investigation. The first of these, which we have used to set up the whole number system in an earlier chapter, is the *successor* function, which is usually denoted by a dash. If we take this function as known, we can then use it to define *addition* by means of the equations

$$a + o = a$$
$$a + b' = (a + b)'.$$

These equations define the function

$$a + b$$

for all values of b, a being any number which we start with. In order to see this we can go one step at a time with b; that is, perform induction on b. When we have defined addition in this way the following scheme

$$a.o = o$$
$$a.b' = a.b + a$$

will serve to define multiplication. (The reader should verify on the one hand that this scheme does correspond to what he intuitively expects to be multiplication, and on the other hand that the product of a and b is defined by this scheme for all values of a and b.) Similarly the scheme

$$a^o = 1$$
$$a^{b'} = a^b.a$$

will define the raising of a to the power b, and the reader should again verify this.

These are all examples which can certainly be calculated for any values of the a and b entering into them, so we can feel sure that if each arithmetical function involves only functions like this, we shall be able to calculate it. But what other functions will be calculable as well? In order to answer this question precisely we must first state what functions (such as the successor function) we shall take as given to start with, and then we must state what operations we expect to carry out on them. We shall do this by defining a set of initial functions and operations which generate what are known as the primitive recursive functions. This class of functions is of great importance in reaching a more general class which seems, as far as we can tell, to correspond to what can be calculated by any means.

The initial functions for the primitive recursive functions are as follows:

(i) the successor function: $f(x) = x'$;

(ii) constant functions of a number of variables whose value is some fixed number, whenever the values of the variables: $f(x_1, x_2, \ldots, x_n) = k$;

(iii) the function whose value for a particular set of variables is one of those variables, say the ith one from the end:

$$f(x_1, x_2, \ldots, x_n) = x_i.$$

These are really our starting point, and now we have also to construct machinery so that we can generate more complicated functions as values:

(iv) a function which is a function of a number of other functions

$$f(x_1, x_2, \ldots, x_n) = g(h_1(x), h_2(x), \ldots, h_m(x))$$

where x stands for all the $x_1, x_2, \ldots, x_n$ and $g, h_1, h_2, \ldots, h_m$ are other functions.

(v) (a) So far we have only defined initial functions. Now we must define the procedure for going up one step at a time; that is, what was referred to before as induction, but in this context is usually called recursion. The simplest case of recursion is one in which the value of the function at the starting point, (o), is given, and then a rule is given for calculating the value of the function at each stage, in terms of its value at the preceding stage, and of the integer labelling the stage with which we are concerned:

$$f(o) = k,$$
$$f(a') = g(a, f(a))$$

where g is a known function. This is a simple case of a more general scheme described in (v) (b):

(v) (b) $f(o, x_2, \ldots, x_n) = g(x_2, \ldots, x_n)$
$f(a', x_2, \ldots, x_n) = h(a, f(a, x_2, \ldots, x_n), x_2, \ldots, x_n)$.

Any function got from these initial functions by means of repeated use of any of them is called a primitive recursive function. A more general concept is that of the general recursive function. We do not wish to enter into the details of these functions here; roughly speaking the general recursive functions are those which can be defined by means of equations in which primitive recursive functions enter.

It is clear that every primitive recursive function is calculable, since we can go up one step at a time. In 1936 Church put forward the suggestion, known now as Church's thesis, that—conversely— every function which is effectively calculable must be generally recursive. We call this hypothesis Church's "thesis" rather than "theorem" since there is no hope of being able to give an exact proof; it states that a class of functions, which have the intuitive— but not formal—property of being somehow or other able to be calculated, is the same as the class of functions with the precise formal property of being generally recursive. Because the idea of being calculable is a vague one, we can only give arguments in favour of Church's thesis, examples which serve to show that all the functions which we would normally think of as calculable are probably general recursive. Arguments of this sort can make Church's thesis plausible (although, as we shall see in the next chapter, there are also arguments on the other side).

At about the same time as Church was formulating his thesis Turing was making an attempt from quite a different direction to say what was effectively calculable. Turing took the more direct line that anything which could be calculated could be calculated by a sufficiently large machine. Nowadays this idea seems rather commonplace, because we have all read of very large machines, and the complicated calculations which they can do. In Turing's time it was much more sensational. We shall consider the machines defined by Turing in the next chapter.

Examples

1. Interpret each stage of the construction of the Gödel unprovable proposition in words and investigate the relationship between this construction and the Cantor diagonal process employed on page 48 of Chapter 4 to show the existence of sets more numerous than the integers.

10 TURING MACHINES

LET US now consider the problem facing a person who has to work out the value of a function of the integers. We can imagine that he has to compute the value for particular integers according to some given set of instructions. When he performs this calculation he must of course use certain distinct symbols (a human operator will for instance use the integers from 0 to 9, together with arithmetical symbols like plus). At any particular moment he can only be looking at a finite set of these symbols. He can, it is true, also remember some previous symbols, as when he is carrying to the next column, but again he can only remember a finite number of such symbols. Likewise the instructions by which he is working must be a finite set of instructions. By applying these instructions to the symbols under observation he can then perform an act which changes the situation. For example he may write down the total, or rub out some symbols which have occurred and then begin to observe other symbols—possibly retaining in his memory those he has observed. The description which we have just given is modelled rather closely on a human operator adding up a column of figures, but it is clear that it represents all calculation to some extent and we naturally want to consider a more general situation.

For example we would like to consider a calculation in general and ask whether we can analyse it into a certain number of basic acts, so that any whole calculation will always be equivalent to some set of basic acts. This analysis was successfully carried out by Turing in 1936—the same year as Church's thesis was formulated. The basic idea of Turing's analysis is that of a *Turing machine*. Such machines do not exist in the sense that actual computers exist; they are ideal machines which we design on paper to carry out the appropriate calculations. The reader who has had cause to learn any thermodynamics will notice that there is a strong analogy here between the part played by the Turing machine and the part played in thermodynamics by the Carnot engine. The Carnot engine could not actually be constructed exactly but we could come very near to it, and by considering its properties we are able to understand the basic principles of thermodynamics. A Turing machine could in principle always be physically constructed, but, because of the extreme simplicity of its method of operation, an actual machine to perform any worthwhile calculation would have to be impossibly large. (This is because we have always a choice in making calculating machines between a machine which works according to very complicated rules which we may perhaps not fully understand, and which accordingly can do complicated calculations of one particular kind although it is a very small machine (e.g. most analogue machines) and machines which work according to very simple methods, which are fully understood, but which will only carry out a large calculation by performing a very large number of basic steps, so that a very large machine is required. The advantage of this second type of machine is that it has very wide possibilities of application, and the Turing machine is a kind of logical limit of all such machines, which is as adaptable as it could possibly be).

Turing derived his concepts by studying actual machines and in order to appreciate his work we shall do the same. The following description is more or less applicable to all large general purpose high speed computers, although it is written from the point of view of one particular machine for the sake of consistency. A computer is a device for performing numerical calculations in just the same way as a human computer. The human computer will need to be given instructions about what to do and also numerical values as data in the calculations. It is worth noticing however that the human computer spends much of his time performing various operations which are not really arithmetical ones at all. The arithmetical operations are all built up out of additions, subtractions and multiplications. But as well as all these operations the computer must record results both in the intermediate stages of the calculation and the final result, look up values for mathematical functions in tables, use previously computed numbers at a later stage in the operation, look up data given at the beginning and of course constantly return to the instructions at each successive stage in the calculation. It will be just the same with an electrical computer. Much of the functioning will be concerned with non-arithmetical operations.

When we described the human computer's operations we mentioned addition, subtraction, multiplication. It is not strictly necessary to include multiplication as a separate function, since it consists of successive addition of one number to another a number of times. However, for the sake of greater speed in the computation it is convenient to include multiplication as a second basic operation. It is usual to express the times for these operations in terms of the microsecond (that is one millionth of a second). Addition and subtraction are operations occupying some one or two hundred microseconds, whilst multiplication takes about twice as long. It is not usually considered worth while to include division as one of the basic operations; instead, one can perform division by successive subtraction of the divisor until a remainder smaller than it is reached.

Let us illustrate our description of a large-scale electric machine by considering the solution of a particular simple problem, say the solution of the two equations

$$ax+by=c$$
$$dx+ey=f$$

The actual procedure for solving these equations is to eliminate y by multiplication and subtraction, deriving as a solution for x the value

$$(ea-db)x=ec-bf$$

How do we solve such a problem as this with the help of the machine? In the first place we must make some provision for putting into the machine the particular problem to be solved, particular problem in this case meaning the values of the coefficients a, b, c, d, e, and f. The machine must have some provision for storing these numbers, and it will in general have a part known as the *store*. We must, of course, be able to retrieve the numbers when we want, so the store will consist of a set of *registers* which are numbered off with numbers known as their *addresses* (just as in a row of houses), each register holding one number. Our instructions to the machine will then begin by ordering the six coefficients to be put in registers 1 . . . 6. As well as storing the numbers the machine must have a part in which it actually performs the operations, and this is usually known as the *accumulator*. The way in which the machine works is to take numbers from the store to the accumulator and perform operations with them, then take the result of this operation back from the accumulator to a suitable location in the store. What happens if the machine tries to put a number into a location in the store which is already occupied? The machine is constructed somewhat like a tape recorder; when a number is inserted into a register the number which is already there, if any, is automatically deleted. It is then not necessary to make any separate provision for deleting numbers in the registers all of which will generally be full.

The way in which the machine operates will be clear from the solution of the rest of the problem. We shall use a number in brackets to denote the address of the corresponding register, and the letter A in brackets to denote the accumulator. We shall also need a notation for the contents of a register and for this we will use the letter C in front of the address. Thus C (2) denotes the contents of register number 2. We begin by taking numbers from the store into the accumulator. Our next instruction, then, is

$$C(1) \rightarrow (A)$$

which signifies that the contents of register 1, that is a, are to be put in the accumulator. (It should be mentioned here that the action of taking the contents of a register is to be interpreted as meaning *taking a copy* of the contents. Register 1 will continue to hold a until such time as something else is put in it.) We now insert the order

$$C(A) \times C(5) \rightarrow (A)$$

which indicates that the contents of the accumulator and the contents of register 5 are to be multiplied together, and the result put in the accumulator. It is necessary, for the sake of simple design of the machine, to put the result of an operation always into the accumulator. If the result needs to be written for later use, as in this case, we shall need to put it into another part of the store and so we have the instruction

$$C(A) \rightarrow (7)$$

We have now finished with the first product in our answer stored in register number 7. The next two instructions form the next product and since the following stage in the calculation will be to subtract this from the previous one we need not store the result but can continue as follows:

$$C(2) \rightarrow (A)$$
$$C(A) \times C(4) \rightarrow (A)$$
$$C(7) - C(A) \rightarrow (A)$$
$$C(A) \rightarrow (9),$$

at the end of which the bracket on the left-hand side of the solution of the equation is stored in register number 9. We now continue with the corresponding expression on the right-hand side and the way of doing this will be obvious:

$$C(3) \rightarrow (A)$$
$$C(A) \times C(5) \rightarrow (A)$$
$$C(A) \rightarrow (7)$$
$$C(6) \rightarrow (A)$$
$$C(A) \times C(4) \rightarrow (8)$$
$$C(7) - C(A) \rightarrow (A)$$
$$C(A) \rightarrow (10)$$

The essential answer is now contained in registers numbers 9 and 10. In order to find the answer to the original problem we only have to divide one of these by the other, and, as we said, although division is not a basic operation it is one which the machine can easily perform by successive subtraction, and for which a set of instructions will already exist.

Turing made an extreme abstraction from all of this. His achievement is the more notable since during his lifetime these machines never reached such a high standard of technical perfection as they have since his death, so that much of his thinking had to be done with plans for a machine rather than the machine itself. Of course such plans go back long before Turing's time. The idea of a large-scale digital computer was actually due to the English mathematician Charles Babbage, at one time professor of mathematics in Cambridge but for most of his life a dedicated gentleman of private means. Babbage hit upon his idea for a digital computer during his attempts to make a much simpler machine which would make tables of mathematical functions automatically by means of differences. When we have a function tabulated at certain intervals we can calculate the differences of the function by subtracting successive values and the differences of those differences and so on. It is found that for most functions the differences at a certain stage tend to be constant over a certain range (a statement which is exactly equivalent to the statement that most functions can be approximated to by polynomials over a certain range). Accordingly if one makes a table with the differences tabulated one can interpolate intermediate values, adding in a portion of the constant differences instead of the whole amount. The following tables will make this clear:

(a)	(b)	(c)	(d)	(e)	(f)
50	6990				
		414			
55	7404		−36		
		378		5	
60	7782		−31		1[−1]
		347		6[4]	
65	8129		−25		−3[−1]
		322		3	
70	8451		−22		
		300			
75	8751				

The first column, (a), are the numbers of which certain functions are calculated in (b); (actually these values are the ordinary logarithms taken from 4-figure tables). The column (c) is now that of first differences; then (d) is the difference of the differences and so on. In the last columns the differences become rather irregular because of errors due to rounding-off (i.e. to using only 4 decimal places) and the figures in brackets denote conjectural "improved" values.

The problem is now to prepare from these figures a table of logarithms for all the integers between 50 and 55. We can set out the initial working as follows:

(a)	(b)	(c)	(d)	(e)	(f)
50	6990				
		—			
51	—		—		
		—			−0.2
52	—		—		
		—			−0.2
53	—		—		
		—			
54	—		—		
		—			
55	7404				
		414	−39/2	6/3	−2/5

At the foot of each column we have set a figure giving the total of the entries to appear there; for column (c) this is evidently 414 from the previous table. For (d) we extrapolate the old differences in (d) and infer that the two opposite the ends of the interval are -36 and -42, so their average is -39. But this is the total for a difference of 10 digits in (a), so it must be halved here. In this way we deduce the totals, and so in column (f) the two entries (since we are taking column (f) as having constant entries). We have to determine the first entry in (e) so as to give the right total. If we suppose it to be 1, as a first guess, the total will come out to

$$1 + 0.8 + 0.6 = 2.4$$

which is 0.4 in excess; but the first entry occurs 3 times here, so we must reduce it by $1/3(0.4) = 0.133$, so it is 0.867. Now (e) may be filled up and the process repeated for (d), (c), and (b) giving (after rounding off!)

(a)	(b)	(c)	(d)	(e)
50	6990			
		93		
51	7083		-6	
		87		1
52	7170		-5	
		82		1
53	7253		-4	
		78		0
54	7330		-4	
		74		
55	7404			

Comparing the results with a table of logarithms shows the greatest error to come for 52 and 53, the error then being about 0.15 per cent.

It is clear that the whole process can be broken down into repeated *additions* of pairs of numbers and Babbage saw that this was a process suitable for mechanisation. Accordingly he tried to construct a machine which would tabulate simple functions to 20 decimal places, having made a pilot model which went up to 8 decimal places. Despite a considerable sum of money (about £17,000) supplied by the government, and a good deal of his own money, Babbage's project was never finished and was finally abandoned by him after about twenty years, because he had realised that his machine was a very special case of a much more interesting device which he called the analytical engine.

According to his son he hit upon the analytical engine by chance when some of the parts of the earlier machine were put together in 1833. He noticed that by inserting a few extra gear wheels (his machine was of course entirely mechanical, somewhat like a modern desk calculator), he could make the result influence the way in which the machine was operating. He then realised that instead of controlling the machine by its results he could make it obey any orders and perform not only additions but other arithmetical processes. He proposed to control the machine by means of a control unit which worked from punched cards. Punched cards had already been used in the early nineteenth century to control the threads in weaving fabrics whose designs were complicated. The punched card idea nowadays is used in modern machines in the form of an input tape with holes punched in it. Such a tape is used to feed in both the numbers and the controlling instructions in a modern machine. The reason that Babbage's ambitious project failed to materialise lies mainly in the relatively primitive state of mechanical engineering in the first half of the nineteenth century, combined with the extreme demands which Babbage's system made on the mechanism. It would probably be possible now to construct Babbage's engine but instead we have electronic machines with no moving parts in the usual sense, the movement being confined to electrical impulses in networks.

Turing was able to see that whether one makes a machine with highly sophisticated mechanical devices which would have been needed to make Babbage's work, or whether one uses electronic equipment, the electronics or the mechanism are just a trick, in a certain very important sense. For the mathematician the vital things in the machine are the input and output tapes, and it is on these that Turing concentrates in his ideal machine. If one were able to try to construct a Turing machine one would need all sorts of highly technical electronic or mechanical devices, but all one is concerned with is what these devices would *do*, and Turing concentrates on this.

Before we can see how Turing applied his analysis to determining what functions can be computed, we must first describe the Turing machine. The description of the machine will be in terms of things which can be physically imagined in an actual machine. The machine has a tape, divided up into squares. It is convenient to describe the tape as infinite; this is simply a shorthand for saying that as well as the instructions in the machine for performing the calculations, there is some device which gives us a warning when we have reached one end or the other of the tape, so that another piece of tape may be fixed on. (We can think of a typewriter in which a bell rings at the end of each line, so that we know when we have to return the carriage to the beginning again. Instead of the bell, we can think of the typewriter typing on an infinite tape.) The tape is, as we said, divided into squares, and each square of the tape can be either blank or have a symbol printed in it. We can, without loss of generality, suppose that only one kind of symbol is used, so that we can use 0 for the content of a blank square and 1 for the content of a printed square. The tape is one square in width, and passes through a scanning device in the machine which reads the content of one square at a time. The machine can be in one of a certain finite list of *states*, and these states determine the action of the machine; designing the machine means giving a list of how it will behave in its various states. The possible behaviour open to the machine when it scans any particular square is as follows: it can either erase the symbol in the square if there is one there, or if the square is blank it can print in it (or it can leave the square unchanged). Having done that it can either continue to scan that square, or it can move to the right by one square, or to the left by one square, and it can change its state from whatever state it is in before it scans the square to a new state, which will depend both on its initial state and on the content of the square (and may, in a special case, be equal to the previous state). All the behaviour of the machine at any stage depends on the state that the machine is in and the content of the square being scanned.

This very simple machine is capable of being adapted to perform, as far as we can see, any calculations which can be performed. In order to perform a calculation, the symbols on the tape must signify numbers in some way. We shall be interested in a machine which will perform calculations involving the positive integers and zero. At first sight it seems as if the blank square should represent zero, but in fact we need blank squares as spaces between numbers. Accordingly we shall represent numbers by rows of printed squares, one printed square by itself representing zero, two together representing 1 and so on. A row of n printed squares then represents the integer $n-1$.

The idea of the Turing machine will become clear if we describe some particular machine, and one of the simplest is the machine whose table is

State	0	1
1	P0	R1

We shall first explain the meaning of the table, and then describe the operation of the machine. The symbols P and E stand for "print" and "erase" (although E does not actually occur in this machine). Similarly L and R stand for "move one place to the left or to the right". The left-hand column of the table is a list of states of the machine; this column for the present simple machine contains only one entry, though we shall describe the machine as having *two* states. The reason for this is that, as well as the states whose characteristics have to be described in the table, there is also one special state called the final state, in which the machine stops because it has carried out the task assigned to it. We shall always distinguish the final state by the number 0, and then number the other states 1, 2, 3, and so on. In the remaining two columns of the table are set down the way that the machine is to behave in the two cases when it reads respectively 0 and 1 in the square which it is scanning (more exactly we should say "when it scans a blank or a printed square"). In this particular table the order to print and erase never occur in the same entry as those to move left or right. When these two kinds of orders do occur together we must adopt some rule about the order in which they are to be carried out. The rule we shall adopt is that the orders to print or erase come first and are to be carried out first, and the orders to move come second and are carried out second. If we then want to print in the next square we must give a new order when the machine has reached it.

The remaining part of the table which we have to describe is the numbers which occur in each place after the orders to print, erase, and move. These numbers denote the state that the machine is to come in after it has performed the earlier orders. The machine begins in an initial state, which we always take as state number one, and for this particular machine this is the only state except for the final state, 0. The orders are that if the machine reads a printed square while it is in this initial state, it moves one place to the right and remains in the same state. If, therefore, it happens to be scanning a row of printed squares without spaces between them it will simply move along all the squares in the sequence until it comes to the end. After it has scanned the last printed square, it moves right once more and then reads a blank square, and so according to the middle column of the table it prints in it and stops. If, then, the machine scans any row of printed squares representing the integer n, it finishes up with the integer $n+1$ on the tape. Thus we have almost described a machine which calculates the successor function (which turns any integer into its successor). We say "almost" because we have to pay attention to whether the machine is in the same state at the beginning as at the end. When the machine stops it is scanning the right-hand square of the row. Actually it is usual to start the machine off scanning the right-hand square of the number with which it is concerned, so that if we start it in this standard position it finishes in the standard position for the new number, and we can then say that, with this convention about standard positions, the machine generates the successor function.

The description of the machine in the last paragraph stated with a given machine, then analysed its behaviour. Naturally we have usually to decide what we want the machine to do, and then design it accordingly. Let us set ourselves the fairly simple problem of designing a machine which will scan a given number, decide whether it is even or odd, and then print 0 or 1 (after a gap) in order to give this information. The machine will begin by scanning the right-hand square of the number, and so in state one we begin (when the square is printed) with the order to move left. At the same time we want to keep a check on whether the number is even or odd, so we introduce a second state of the machine—two—and order the machine to go into this other state. In state two the machine is to continue to move left so long as it reads a printed square, but is to go back into state one again. In this way the machine moves one step at a time along the row of printed squares, being alternatively in states one and two until it gets to the first zero. Let us begin by supposing that we are dealing with an even number, which is (therefore) represented by an odd number of printed squares, so that the machine first reads a zero when it is in state two. If this happens we know that we have an even number, and we just have to arrange for the machine to go to the right-hand end, leave a space, and print 1. We can do this by an order to move right and go into state three, while in state three—whenever the square is occupied—it is always to move right, and then continue in state three. In this way the machine will move one step at a time to the right-hand end of the number, and then one step more, so that it reads 0. This first blank square is the one we want to leave as a gap, so we must again order the machine to move right, and we must also introduce another state, so that we can order the machine to print: call this state four. If the machine now encounters a blank square in state four, it has to print and stop. (If, of course, it encounters a printed square in state four, it is unable to carry out the calculations suggested because some tape which has already been used has been put into the machine.)

We must now come back to the possibility of the original number being odd, so that the machine first scans a blank square when it is in state one. Here, then, we must introduce another state which we can call five, and order the machine to move to the right, staying in that state until it reaches a blank square. This blank square is the gap which we must leave, and then we have to print in two squares. The reader can verify that the following table carries out this calculation as we have described.

State	0	1
1	$R5$	$L2$
2	$R3$	$L1$
3	$R4$	$R3$
4	$P0$	
5	$R6$	$R5$
6	$PR4$	

In order to understand the construction of more complicated Turing machines we shall now describe one more which performs an operation frequently used in calculation. This is the machine for closing up a row of numbers. We could imagine an initial situation on the tape like

1 0 0 0 0 1 1 1 0

and the problem is to move the right-hand number up to the left until it is next to it (with of course a gap to separate them) as in the following

1 0 1 1 1 0 0 0 0 .

This is a more complicated machine because we now have to erase some of the printing and print it elsewhere.

In designing the machine it is easy enough to begin. We scan the right-hand square, and since this has to be removed we first erase it and then move left. At the same time we change the state of the machine and continue to move left until the point where we first reach a blank square. In this blank square we may then print the symbol which is instead of the one we erased. Now the more difficult part of the procedure begins. We can carry out this process one step at a time, which has the effect of moving the number up one step at a time, but we must not go too far. We must make sure that when we have printed the new symbol there is still a blank space to the left of it, and so accordingly we insert the order to move left, and now we go into a new state, three, whose job is to read whether or not there is a space to the left. If there is a space all is well, so we go to the right, one space at a time, until we get to the right-hand end of the number, and having got there (and one step past it, so as to read o and so *know* that we have got there), we move left and begin the whole process over again, by putting the machine in state one.

If, however, when this process has been carried out a number of times, we find that, after the last printing, we move left and then read a one, this means that we have gone one step too far. We then order the machine into a new state, five, whose purpose is simply to correct each error; that is, we erase the one we have just printed and move to the right, which puts right half the error we have made. The other half which remains to be tackled is caused by the fact that we erased one too many symbols at the beginning, so that the new state, six, contains orders to move to the right, remaining always in the same state, until the first step at which we reach a blank square. This blank square is the one which ought to have been printed, and so we give the order to print and then to stop, since the whole operation has now been carried out. The results of the argument are summarised in the following table

State	0	1
1		EL2
2	PL3	L2
3	R4	R5
4	L1	R4
5		ER6
6	P0	R6

In this table there are two blank spaces, but one—corresponding to reading a blank square when in state one—occurs because state one is the initial state, and the machine cannot be scanning a blank square in its initial state (can you prove this?). The other blank square corresponds to the fact that the machine can never get into state five and be scanning a blank square. The reader may also care to satisfy himself about this. The machines which we have constructed are all fairly simple machines; to make a more complicated machine it is usually best not to construct the whole machine afresh as in the arguments given here, but first to break up the calculation into smaller pieces, like the calculations given here (for example, adding one or closing up, and similar simple operations) and then when the machines have been constructed for these simple operations we can join them together by making the terminal state of one machine the initial state of the next one, renumbering all the states accordingly. The reader should set himself the problem of constructing a machine which will add together two numbers written next to each other on the tape. (If the numbers were not written next to each other we could first close them up by means of the machine in this paragraph.) The machine has to erase *two* printed squares from the right-hand end and fill in the gap between the two numbers. (Why?)

The previous paragraphs have shown how we can go about constructing machines to do particular calculations. Turing, as a result of his analysis (of which a sketch was given at the beginning of this chapter) put forward the hypothesis that any function for which a rule could be given for calculation could be calculated on a Turing machine. This hypothesis has in many ways a much more direct intuitive appeal than Church's thesis, since Turing machines obviously bear a close resemblance to the actual large computing machines to which we are now used. Moreover, they are simpler in their construction and therefore even more adaptable. However, it is a fact that Church's thesis and Turing's hypothesis are exactly equivalent; that is, the functions which can be calculated by Turing machines are exactly the generally recursive functions. It is obvious that any machine which we can construct will produce a general recursive function, since the machine operations are certainly no more complicated than those used to define recursive functions. To prove the equivalence of the two hypotheses the other way round is naturally a much more detailed process; we have in fact to show that every general recursive function can be computed, and we do this by actually constructing the Turing machines corresponding to the basic primitive recursive functions of the last chapter. We already have one such machine available—the one corresponding to the successor function. Unfortunately this machine is very much simpler than those needed for the other functions. It would take us beyond the subject matter of the present book to go into the details of the construction of these machines, but it should be clear from the last few paragraphs the general way in which we can go about it.

Instead it is more appropriate to present some of the arguments against Church's thesis or Turing's hypothesis, if only to show that not everyone is agreed about this criterion of what can be calculated. The following paradoxical argument is due to Kalmar. We begin with a function which has already been shown by Kleene to be not generally recursive. In order to define this function we use a generally recursive function, f, of two arguments, x and y. We define the Kleene function $g(x)$ of x by the rule

$$g(x) = \begin{cases} \text{The least } y \text{ for which } f(x, y) = 0 \text{ if such a } y \text{ exists,} \\ 0, \text{ if no } y \text{ exists for which } f(x, y) = 0. \end{cases}$$

We shall assume here Kleene's result that this function is not generally recursive. As a consequence of Church's thesis this function cannot be effectively calculated; that is, we have no rule which will always provide for its calculation. This consequence of Church's thesis has some rather strange results.

First suppose that p is a positive integer for which, as it happens, there is a y for which $f(p, y) = 0$. We can then find the least such y by calculating in succession $f(p, 0), f(p, 1), f(p, 2) \ldots$ (since f is generally recursive), and so $g(p)$ is known. On the other hand suppose that, for a particular integer p, we can prove by *any* correct arguments (N.B. not within some previously defined formal system as with Gödel's theorem!) that no integer y exists for which $f(p, y) = 0$; then, again, $g(p)$ is calculable (since it is 0).

However, from Kleene's result (and Church's thesis) there must be at least one integer p for which (i) there is no integer y for which $f(p, y) = 0$ (since otherwise we would have the first case above and (ii) this fact cannot be established for p by *any* correct means (since otherwise we should have the second case above). Consider then the proposition, for this particular value of p, "There is a natural number y such that $f(p, y) = 0$". This proposition cannot be proved or disproved, but as we said before, this is not in the sense of a particular formal system as with Gödel's theorem, but by any correct means. We know we cannot prove the proposition, since it is false; but we cannot disprove it since we cannot prove its negation. We have, it seems, an *absolutely undecidable* proposition, as a consequence of Church's thesis.

Yet this absolutely undecidable proposition seems too good to be true, and so it is; for we *can* decide it—we know it is false! Such

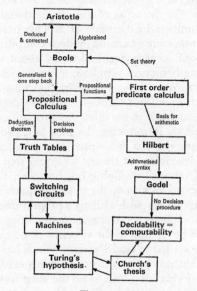

Figure 10.

a paradox* may well seem the most fitting end to our survey of man's attempts to make his discourse more and more precise.

Let us now stand back and survey the territory which we have covered in this book. In following this summary *Figure 10* will be a helpful guide. We began our study of formal systems with Aristotle's attempt. When this attempt is put into algebraic form one has the algebra devised by Boole (Chapter 3). Conversely, from Boole's algebra one can deduce Aristotle's logic in a corrected form. However, it is not possible simply to go on from there because both Boole and Aristotle have begun a little too far along the line. In a more

* It is not suggested that this is a paradox, like those of set theory, which we cannot remove; but removing it would take us beyond the scope of this book.

general formulation beginning one stage back, we have the propositional calculus discussed in Chapter 5 dealing with propositions in their own right and irrespective of their structure. From here the path divides. The deduction theorem for the propositional calculus leads to the truth tables of Chapter 6, and these in turn are shown by the solution of the decision problem to lead back to the propositional calculus. These truth tables can be realised electrically by means of switching circuits, and these circuits used to construct machines either to do logic (in the sense of the propositional calculus) or to compute with numbers in the scale of 2. This particular development is of great importance because modern computers have affected our thoughts about what is decidable, and about what constitutes a solution of a mathematical problem, so profoundly.

Let us now return to the propositional calculus and look at the other path which goes from there. In order to do genuine mathematics we have to have more than the propositional calculus, so this is generalised by introducing the idea of a propositional function. We then have the first order predicate calculus, and since this is adequate for describing set theory we could step back to Boole's algebra again if we wished. Going on, however, the fact that the first order predicate calculus ought to be adequate for constructing arithmetic ties up closely with Hilbert's programme for formalising mathematics. Since however the system describes arithmetic, and at the same time the syntax of the system can be specified in terms of arithmetic, we are led to Gödel's result, which has as a by-product the conclusion that no decision procedure can exist for the system. Indeed, what is decidable is seen to be the same as what is computable, so that we are involved in the problem considered by Church and Turing of what can be computed. Church's thesis is an attempt to answer this problem from a logical point of view, and it is known to be completely equivalent to Turing's answer. Turing, however, devised his answer by studying actual computing machines, so that we find that we have gone round in a complete circle; the ideas which one path led up to are also of importance in understanding the other.

Examples

1. Carry out the suggestion on page 119.
2. Construct a machine which, given two numbers x, y next to each other on the tape, prints $x - y$ to the right of y, if $x > y$, and prints zero otherwise.

INDEX